The Dartmoor Tin Industry

A Field Guide

by Phil Newman

1998

First published in Great Britain in 1998 by Chercombe Press, PO Box 30,
Newton Abbot, Devon, TQ12 1XT UK

ISBN 0 9532708 0 7

Printed by Short Run Press, Sowton Exeter, Devon

Cover photo: *View across the tin openworks at Birch Tor, including Chaw Gully*

CONTENTS

LIST OF ILLUSTRATIONS

LIST OF PLATES

Preface

This book is intended to fill a long neglected though very important gap in the literature of Dartmoor. Many books have been written about Dartmoor the place, among which many mention the tin industry: few however have attempted to explain the field remains in detail and even fewer still have concentrated on this subject alone. Several books have supplied excellent introductions to Dartmoor's industrial past, such as Helen Harris's *Industrial Archaeology of Dartmoor*[1], which offers an authoritative, general description. R.H. Worth[2] provided a sound basis for the study of early tin mills while Hamilton Jenkin[3], P.H.G. Richardson[4] and Tom Greeves[5] have provided detailed works on the later mines of Dartmoor. More recently Sandy Gerrard has discussed aspects of the tin industry within the context of landscape archaeology[6]. Much additional information has been published in learned journals which are not so easily accessible to those with only a casual interest and a further layer of important academic research is not available in any published form. In Cornwall, where the tin industry has been of greater economic importance than in Devon, archaeological and historical investigation have supplied additional important data.

Altogether, a good body of well-researched information now exists but, although the Dartmoor tin industry has been studied by archaeologists for a little over 100 years, until now no general guide has been published. The present work brings together much of the currently available information into one book of reference.

This is a field guide and as such is only concerned with field evidence or that which remains to be seen on Dartmoor today. Historical evidence, although used in the introduction and to supply background to interpretation of the remains, is not covered as a subject in itself, as it could theoretically fill a book in its own right. Details of underground mining, which we are today unable to explore are also not discussed. Some aspects of the field evidence have received greater attention by past researchers than others and the body of data available has a commensurate imbalance, reflected to some extent in the present work in that tin mills are discussed in finer detail than some other aspects. This imbalance will hopefully be corrected in the future as more research is carried out.

Geologically the Devonian and Cornish tinfields offer a similar resource, and discussing the archaeology of either on its own is certainly only·telling half the story, especially in view of the volume of recent work undertaken by Cornish archaeologists and the scale of the industry in that county. However, Dartmoor is a very special place archaeologically, containing clear evidence on the ground of over 4000 years of human activity, of which tin extraction forms one part. This fact coupled with the accessibility of much of Dartmoor has led to it becoming a popular destination for people to explore, often seeking information about what they see and a guide to the tin industry of Dartmoor only is justified, though a work which brings together the tinworking histories of both counties is still very much needed.

If I have learned one thing above any other from compiling this book it is that generalisations are usually disprovable by the exceptions, but as space forbids highly detailed or deeply analytical discussion of every facet of the subject, a general approach to the explanation of each category of remains has to suffice. However, the bibliography at the rear of the guide offers a good basis for further reading.

Examples of all the types of field evidence described in the text are provided with grid references at the end of each chapter. Where possible, and in nearly all cases, the sites described are on open moorland with free access at the time of writing. However, to illustrate one or two points it has been necessary to cite examples which are on private land and the owner's permission must be sought before visiting these sites.

Acknowledgments

I am most grateful to Dr Sandy Gerrard for reading through the text and suggesting many improvements; also for granting permission to adapt his survey of Lydford Woods (Fig. 3) for my own purposes. Similarly I am grateful to the Dartmoor Tinworking Research Group for allowing use of the Beckamoor Combe and Upper Merrivale material(Figs 4 & 10); the Royal Commission on the Historical Monuments of England (Figs 7 & 20); Frances Griffith (Plate 1) and Torquay Natural History Society(Fig. 2). Thanks to Rob Wilson-North for checking and commenting on the final draft of the text. Although the compilation and writing of this guide has been very much a personal effort, clearly I owe an enormous debt to the many other archaeologists and historians who have researched the subject, past and present, and who collectively are responsible for our understanding of the subject today: this I wish to acknowledge.

(For references see page 10)

1

Introduction

Dartmoor is the South-West's largest tract of upland and since 1951 has been one of Britain's eleven National Parks. Besides its rugged natural beauty and the feeling of remoteness it provides for those who explore it, the area has long been renowned for the number and extent of its archaeological remains, possessing one of the most intact prehistoric landscapes anywhere in Europe. The enigmatic stone rows and circles, burial sites, houses, farmsteads and field systems of farmers who inhabited the area some 4000 years ago, are easily observed by those who explore the moor today and they have fascinated archaeologists for over two centuries.

Medieval farmers also lived and worked on Dartmoor, and there is evidence of their activity from as early as the 8th century AD some scholars have argued[1]. The long, stone-faced banks which enclosed their small isolated farmsteads, mostly date from the 12th century or later and although some of the farms were abandoned long ago, many others remain occupied today, in only a slightly altered form.

Shoddily built dry-stone walls, now in a crumbling and often derelict state, supply testament to a more recent period of rather optimistic and grandiose agricultural schemes of the 18th and 19th centuries.

Though appearing to be wilderness and often referred to as such by protagonists from both sides of the conservation debate, the landscape of Dartmoor as it appears today is very much a product of humans. Dartmoor's very special asset is that the evidence of so many episodes of past human activity survive.

Besides pastoral and agricultural uses, Dartmoor has seen intense periods of industrial activity, exploiting the area's rich natural resources, such as peat, granite, clay and metals. Digging and mining for tin, the richest of these metals, has arguably had the most dramatic effect of all human activities, on how the uplands of Dartmoor appear today, with extensive areas of the moor permanently scarred and changed. Only time and nature's ability to smooth over the scars have helped disguise the evidence of massive opencast pits and many hectares of spoil heaps, along with buildings, water courses and processing areas.

When archaeologists first began to investigate Dartmoor, over 200 years ago,the tin industry was still operational and an interest in its past was restricted only to speculation as to its earliest origins. Tin is the second ingredient of bronze, the main ingredient being copper and it did not escape the notice of early scholars that both metals occur close by in south-west England. Although the term 'Bronze Age' was not in use until the 1820s, the discovery of bronze artefacts by antiquaries investigating ancient burial sites, assumed to be pre-Roman in date, fueled the argument for prehistoric exploitation of tin on Dartmoor. The 18th-century historian and traveller Richard Polwhele was among the earliest antiquaries to equate the remains of tin streamworks on Dartmoor with the prehistoric period when he wrote in 1797:

> *In the parishes of Manaton, Kingsteignton, and Teigngrace, are many old Tin-works of this kind, which the inhabitants attribute to that period, when wolves and winged serpents were no strangers to the hills or the valleys... and indeed all the valleys from the Heathfield to Dartmoor, bear the traces of shoding and streaming; which; I doubt not, was either British or Phenician*[2]

This was not an entirely new idea however, as the belief that Phoenicians (from the area now known as the Lebanon in the Middle-East) had been trading the metals of south-west Britain had been around for some time. It was based on the fanciful assumptions of even earlier writers and is completely unsupported either archaeologically or by sound historical evidence.

The suggestion that tin extraction was occurring in the South-West and on Dartmoor in prehistory has persisted even until the present day and is indeed difficult to argue against despite the great lack of reliable archaeological evidence. Nearly all scholars interested in prehistoric Dartmoor have had to wrestle with this possibility and some have concluded that if tinworking had been occurring then we have been unable to find evidence for it because later tinners have re-worked the same tinworks and destroyed such evidence as we should expect to find. Others such as Robert Burnard, a major figure in the early exploration of Dartmoor's antiquities, believed that the absence of any real evidence for very early tinworking on Dartmoor, must mean that the industry had its beginnings after the Roman occupation. [3]

Although in Cornwall some prehistoric artefact finds in tin streamworks offer possible evidence of early activity, on Dartmoor a single piece of tinstone, found during the excavation of a prehistoric hut circle on Dean Moor, is the only evidence to support the claim so far.[4] Nevertheless, today it is probably sensible to take a more flexible view of the issue and concede that given the high level of settlement in a rich tin bearing area during a period when tin was a valued commodity, it is unlikely that the population were unaware of, or did not exploit the resource. It is perhaps only a matter of time before reliable evidence is presented, particularly as early metallurgy becomes the subject of the scientific research techniques now available to archaeologists.

Serious antiquarian investigation of the Dartmoor tin industry began in the second half of the 19th century, when writers started questioning the function and date of the small rectangular structures we know today as tin mills or 'blowing houses'. First among these was John Kelly who in 1866 examined the lower mill at Yealm Steps, concluding that the site was associated with tin smelting[5].

The first detailed examination of a mill was undertaken by Robert Burnard in the 1880s when he 'cleared' the interior of the lower mill at Week Ford[6]. The somewhat inconclusive results sparked off a debate as to the function of the artefacts found, but with the level of interest now raised, others began to investigate tin mills. Most notable among these researchers was R. Hansford Worth who, between 1892 and 1946, made detailed records of over 40 sites, establishing many of the facts we now possess about tin mills[7]. Until the 1970s, 20 years after his death, Worth's work more or less stood alone for much of the 20th century and he has certainly made one of the greatest individual contributions to the study of this subject.

More recently the Dartmoor tin industry has come to the attention of the trained archaeologist including Tom Greeves, who adopted Dartmoor tin for his doctoral thesis, in 1981[8]. Since then the study has gained further momentum with the formation of the Dartmoor Tinworking Research Group in 1991, one of whose objectives has been the excavation of a tin mill. Tinworkings are also now recorded by the Royal Commission on the Historical Monuments of England, who have been systematically mapping the archaeology of Dartmoor since the late 1980s, and the tin industry has become an integral part of more focused landscape studies on Dartmoor, such as that currently in progress in the Meavy Valley by Dr Sandy Gerrard.

Despite this level of attention it is surprising how much we have yet to find answers to, especially about the earlier techniques of tin extraction, the knowledge of which has been lost to us. Many pieces of evidence still defy easy explanation but new discoveries and new observations lead to fresh interpretations continually being made and much knowledge has been gained in the years since serious investigation began.

HISTORICAL BACKGROUND

Tin has been a much sought after material since prehistoric times when, among other uses, it was alloyed with copper to form bronze. Tin-bronze artefacts were in use in Europe by at least 2000 BC and examples of prehistoric metalwork have been found in Devon, although for the reasons discussed above we cannot be certain that the tin used in these artefacts was local. Bronze has to this day remained among the major uses for tin. By medieval times there was also a huge demand for tin in the production of pewter, an alloy of tin and lead, which was, from the 13th century onwards, the most important material used in the manufacture of domestic metal wares, such as bowls, drinking vessels and spoons. Its significance in the 17th century can be gauged by the estimate that for every man woman and child in the country at that time, there was on average twelve pounds of pewter in circulation[9]. Although seldom used on its own, tin has always been a key ingredient of alloying, used not only in bronze and pewter but also for materials as diverse in use (though similar in makeup) as organ pipe metal and solder. From the 19th century onwards the tinplate industry provided

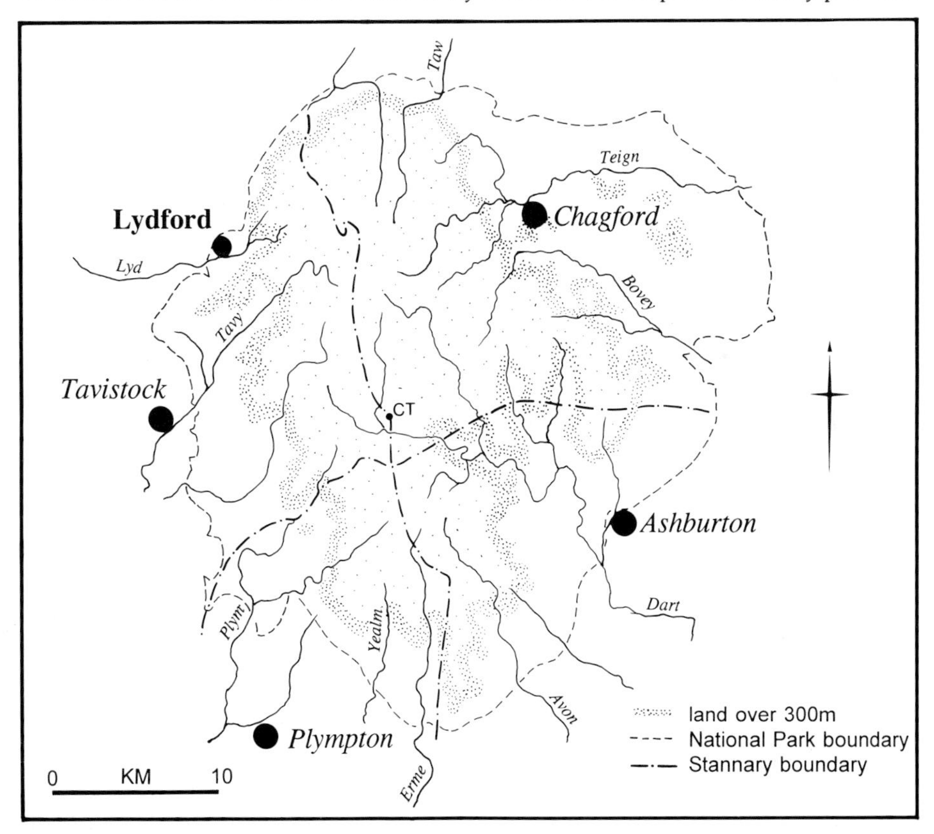

Fig. 1. Map of Dartmoor National Park showing land over 300m; principal rivers; the Stannary Towns and boundaries; Lydford, site of the Stannary Gaol; Crockerntor(CT), meeting place of the Stannary Parliament.

further demand for tin fueled by the advent of canned produce. Though the demand for tin remains to the present day, much of this is now met by cheaper sources from elsewhere in the world such as Malaysia and Brazil. Tin has not been worked commercially in Devon since the 1930s and at the time of writing only one tin mine remains in production in Cornwall, though its future is very much in question.

Our earliest surviving documents testifying to the working of tin on Dartmoor are from the 12th century, but by the 13th century specific tinworks were being referred to by name. Among these is 'la Dryeworke' (Dry Lake) mentioned as part of the bounds of the Forest of Dartmoor in 1240[10]. However, we know for certain the industry was well established much earlier than that because of the records of tin production figures from the 12th century and it is very likely that the earliest origins of the medieval tin industry extend back much further than hitherto revealed by surviving documentation. The production figures, which were recorded by officials of the Stannaries, offer a good guide to the fortunes of the industry with production exceeding even that of Cornwall for a brief period in the 12th century. After about 1400 production was again on the increase, reaching a peak in 1524, thereafter to decline over the next century to virtually nothing by 1650. A short renaissance at around 1700 had again faded by 1740[11]. Subsequently the figures are not recorded for Dartmoor as a whole and

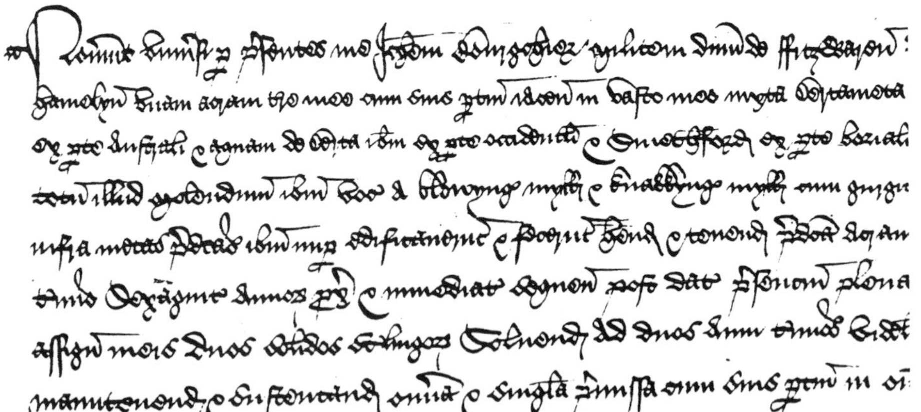

Fig. 2. Extract from a lease of land to Christopher Prouse and Richard Hemelyn who had recently built a blowing and a knacking mill at Dartmeet 'totum illud molendinium ibidem vocatum a blowyng myll & knakkyng myll' 1514 (DRO 48/14/40/3)(Reproduced with permission of Torquay Natural History Society).

although tin was mined there for much of the 19th and early 20th century, production is likely to have been negligible compared to that of three centuries earlier.

The Stannaries were the districts into which Devon and Cornwall were divided for the purpose of administration of the tin industry. The county of Devon as a whole was divided into four such districts, although in reality tin was only exploited on and around Dartmoor itself. The Stannaries, named after their administrative centres, were Tavistock, Chagford, Ashburton and Plympton. At each town tin smelted within its area of jurisdiction would be taken for 'coinage', where it was weighed and its owner then had to pay the appropriate taxation to the crown. It is likely also that traders dealing in tin would operate from the Stannary towns. Detailed records survive and have been published for the Tavistock Coinage of 1523, revealing fascinating information about the names of tinners, where they lived and the quantities of tin they presented.[12]

The Devon tinners worked within their own system of legislation and their activities were not subject to Common Law but Stannary Law, a privilege granted to them by the Crown on account of the massive revenue that the tin industry could bring in taxation. Their special laws were enacted at parliaments or 'Great Courts' held at Crockerntor, a bleak granite outcrop on central Dartmoor. Jurates, or representatives from each of the Stannaries, would attend the courts to discuss the day-to-day affairs of the industry, and to create new legislation regarding matters such as staking claims for tin workings, diverting water supplies and methods of disposing of waste. They could also settle disputes among tinners or between tinners and landowners. Serious contraventions of the tinners' laws could result in imprisonment in the infamous Stannary gaol at Lydford; a square 13th-century castle keep which still stands today. We do not know how often these courts took place but 13 were recorded between 1474 and 1786 and its likely that there were others for which record does not survive.[13]

There is a fair quantity of surviving documentation concerning the individual tinworks and tin mills after about 1500. Most of these are share documents which list the shareholders, tell us the name of the site and very often describe the location and extent of the working. Some of these place names have survived to the present day and we can identify 'Classiwell' for example, mentioned in 1625 as being in the vicinity of Classiwell Farm in the Newleycombe Valley[14]. It is clear from the documentation that some tinworks were worked for a considerable period of time. Keaglesborough, a large openwork, also in the Newleycombe Valley, is first mentioned in 1505 when it was said to have been 'long time in dispute' but its most recent date is 1639 giving it at least a 140 year working life, though of course it may not have been active through the whole of that period.[15] For some tin mills we also have documents such as leases (Fig. 2) which among other things can tell us if the mills were used for crushing ('knacking mills') or smelting ('blowing mills'). This is very useful because at some sites there may be no visible archaeological evidence by which these facts may be determined.

The owners of tinworks themselves represented a cross-section of late medieval society ranging from minor gentry to tenant farmers; even the Abbot of Buckland possessed tinworking shares[16]. One study, set on south-west Dartmoor has demonstrated that for every farm investigated in the area(14 in total), at least one tinner had resided there at some time in the period from about 1450 to 1700[17]. It is perhaps also likely that these people were a major source of labour for the industry, supplementing their income with earnings from tinworking.

Although these documents can provide detailed information about particular sites and tinners, they supply little in the way of background to help us understand how tin was worked and processed, which in turn would give clues to the interpretation of that which remains today. Most contemporary travellers and writers seem not to have bothered recording observations about tinworking in Devon either and those that did, contribute little to our understanding of the field remains. Our major source for this kind of material therefore comes from the accounts of Cornish observers such as Richard Carew, Thomas Beare and William Pryce, whose valuable works will be referred to in later chapters.

For the later period of Dartmoor's tinworking history, between about 1800 and 1933 the documentary record, where surviving, can be a little more informative, although the influence of the Stannaries had by this time declined quite considerably with the last parliament held in 1786,[18] so this very useful source of general information is unavailable after that date. Apart from legal and business documents, sale particulars and inventories where companies have been wound up, sometimes survive as do plans of mine setts, records of wages and purchases. However, all these sources are still very fragmentary and for many tin mines documentation eludes us though clear evidence may survive in the field. Fortunately, for some of the later mines we have photographs and oral record from people who worked in the mines or remember the mines at work. Many mines have been the subject of detailed historical research in recent years, such as Steeperton Tor Mine[19], Eylesbarrow Mine[20], Wheal Cumpston[21] and Brimpts[22].

Historical research has done much to shed light on many important aspects of the tin industry from earliest recorded times onwards, allowing us major insights into the social and economic background of the tinners, as well as supplying some clues about the remains they left behind on the moors. However, it is by field investigation that we can really begin to understand the extent and complexity of this once thriving industry and it is this which the reader is encouraged to do. Aided by this guide, understanding the evidence will hopefully be easier.

References

1. Fleming & Ralph 1982
2. Polwhele 1797, 158
3. Burnard 1911, 50-51
4. Fox 1957, 73
5. Kelly 1866, 46
6. Burnard 1887-90, 226-7
7. Worth 1953, 289-328
8. Greeves 1981
9. Homer 1995, 57
10. Moore & Birkett 1890, 6, 53
11. Worth 1953, 287
12. Finberg 1949, 155-184
13. Greeves 1987, 145-167
14. Newman 1994, 227
15. ibid, 227
16. Greeves 1987a, 239
17. Newman 1994, 230-2
18. Greeves 1987, 161
19. Greeves 1985, 101-127
20. Cook et al 1974, 161-214
21. Greeves 1978, 161-171
22. Bird & Hirst 1997

References for Preface (from page 2)

1. Harris 1968
2. Worth 1953
3. Hamilton Jenkin 1974
4. Richardson 1992
5. Greeves 1986
6. Gerrard 1997a

2

Extraction

The history of extractive techniques used to win tin from Dartmoor is very much one of a progression, dictated by the types of ore available to each generation of tinners and the technology they were able to develop. Success by medieval and earlier tin streamers at harvesting the rich and more easily accessible alluvial deposits led to those sources becoming more scarce, creating a need to exploit the parent tin lodes. Far greater effort was involved in excavating the massive openworks needed to do this but, judging by the number of these workings visible on Dartmoor, the process was certainly considered worthwhile. However, once the shallower lode deposits had been worked out, the search for tin needed to go deeper and underground mining techniques were developed in the 18th and 19th centuries. This does not however, preclude the use of underground mining before this time, which certainly was occurring as early as the 15th century[1], elsewhere in Devon and in Europe for other types of ore as well as tin, but until we have evidence to the contrary, its use seems unlikely to have been widespread for tin on Dartmoor, while the more accessible sources were still available nearby.

STREAMWORKS

The method used to exploit the rich alluvial deposits found at the bottom of river valleys was known as streamworking or streaming. These deposits were formed by cassiterite (tin oxide) which had become detached from the lodes through weathering, to be transported into the river beds by various geological agencies. Once detached from the lode, these same agencies separated the cassiterite from other minerals during transportation, to deposit very pure tin gravel into the river valleys. To exploit this source, it was necessary for the tinners to sort the tin from the other unwanted gravels, such as mica, feldspar and quartz (collectively known as gangue), which had been deposited by the same means alongside the tin. This was achieved by taking advantage of the large disparity between the specific gravity of cassiterite, which varies between 6.8 and 7.1, and the gangue materials which are typically between 2.5 and 3[2]. If

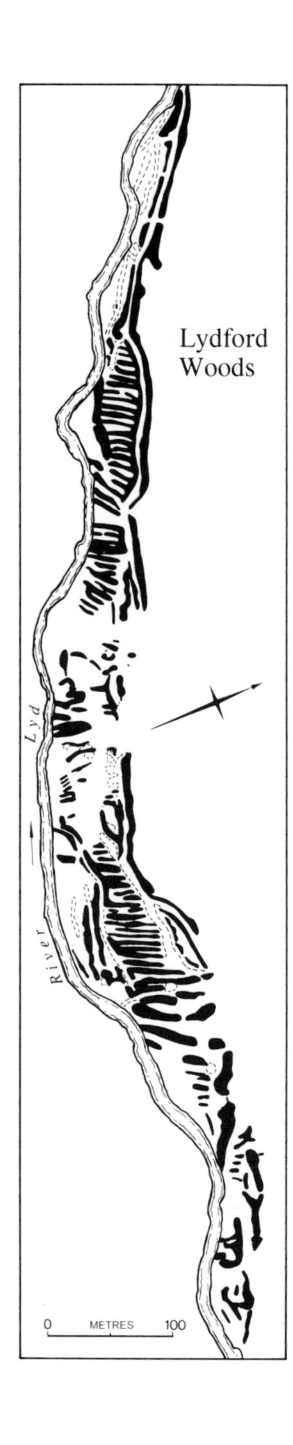

moving water was passed over an exposed deposit, the lighter waste materials would be washed away much faster than the heavier tin ore which could be separated out.

The extraction of tin by streaming in some form would have been familiar to prehistoric tinners, though remains of their activities have not yet been recognised on Dartmoor. There is also good reason to believe that a thriving tin industry could have been in existence here during the Dark Ages too though again, archaeological evidence for this has so far proved elusive. The majority of the streamworks which remain to be observed today are likely to date from a period of recorded prosperity between the 11th and 18th century, although no earthwork evidence has yet been precisely dated.

Detailed contemporary accounts of the methods employed by the tin streamers of Devon are not known to have survived. Travellers and writers such as Leland[3] and Risdon[4] mentioned streamworking in their general descriptions of the county but failed to describe the working techniques. The Cornish record is a little more instructive but details for the early period are still very fragmentary and it is not until 1778 that we have a description from William Pryce, in his comprehensive work, *Mineralogia Cornubiensis*[5]. However, the most useful account of streamworking technique comes from Hitchens' and Drew's *History of Cornwall* of 1824, which although much later than the probable working

Fig. 3. Simplified plan of earthworks at Lydford Woods alluvial tin streamwork (SX 494 837), demonstrating the systematic dumping of spoil in rib-like arrangements of linear banks (after Gerrard 1996). For key see Fig. 4. N.B. this tinwork is on land currently under ownership of the National Trust and Forest Enterprises.

lives of the majority of Dartmoor's streamworks is still relevant because the essential basis behind the methods is likely to have remained relatively unchanged.

> *..When thus discovered, the first step taken by the tinner is to procure from the land-owner, or bounder, or both, a right to work. This right is called a sett. This being ratified agreeably to the rules prescribed by the stannary laws, a stream of water is conducted on the surface to the spot where he intends to begin his operations. a level is also brought home to the spot from below, as deep as the ground will permit, and the workings require, to carry off the sand and water. The ground is then opened at the extremity nearest the sea, or the discharge of the water; from which place the streamers (for by this name the tinners are known to distinguish them from miners) proceed towards the hill. On the ground which is laid open, the stream of water is turned in from the surface, which, running over an almost perpendicular descent, washes off the lighter parts of such ground as had been previously broken by picks, carrying them through the under level, which is called the tye, and leaving behind the sandy ore, and such stones as are too heavy to thus be removed. In this stream the men, provided with boots for the purpose, continue to stand, keeping the sand and gravel at the bottom in motion. From it they select the larger rubbish, throwing it on one side, picking from their shovels such shode as appears. The precipice over which the water runs is called the breast; the rubbish thrown away is called stent; the sand, including tin, is called the gard; the walls on each side of the tye are called stiling; and the more worthless parts which are driven away by the stream are called tailings. In this manner they continue to dig or break the ground until the whole is exhausted, which is sometimes the work of many years.*[6]

Field remains of alluvial streamworks are widely distributed over much of Dartmoor where river valleys untouched by streaming activity are quite rare. Typically a streamwork will occupy a thin band of ground on either or both sides of the smaller, more steeply inclined streams, such as Brim Brook, though in the more level planes of the larger rivers such as at Taw Marsh, or along the River Dart and the River Plym, the tinworked area may be much more expansive, extending for 100m or more from the stream.

The edge of a streamwork is usually marked by a scarp, delineating the limit of extractive activity, which, depending on the depth to which the tin was worked,

Fig. 4. Simplified plan of earthworks at Beckamoor Combe eluvial tin streamwork (SX 5350 7500), showing position of reservoirs and water channels, and areas of systematic spoil dumping. (After a survey by DTRG).

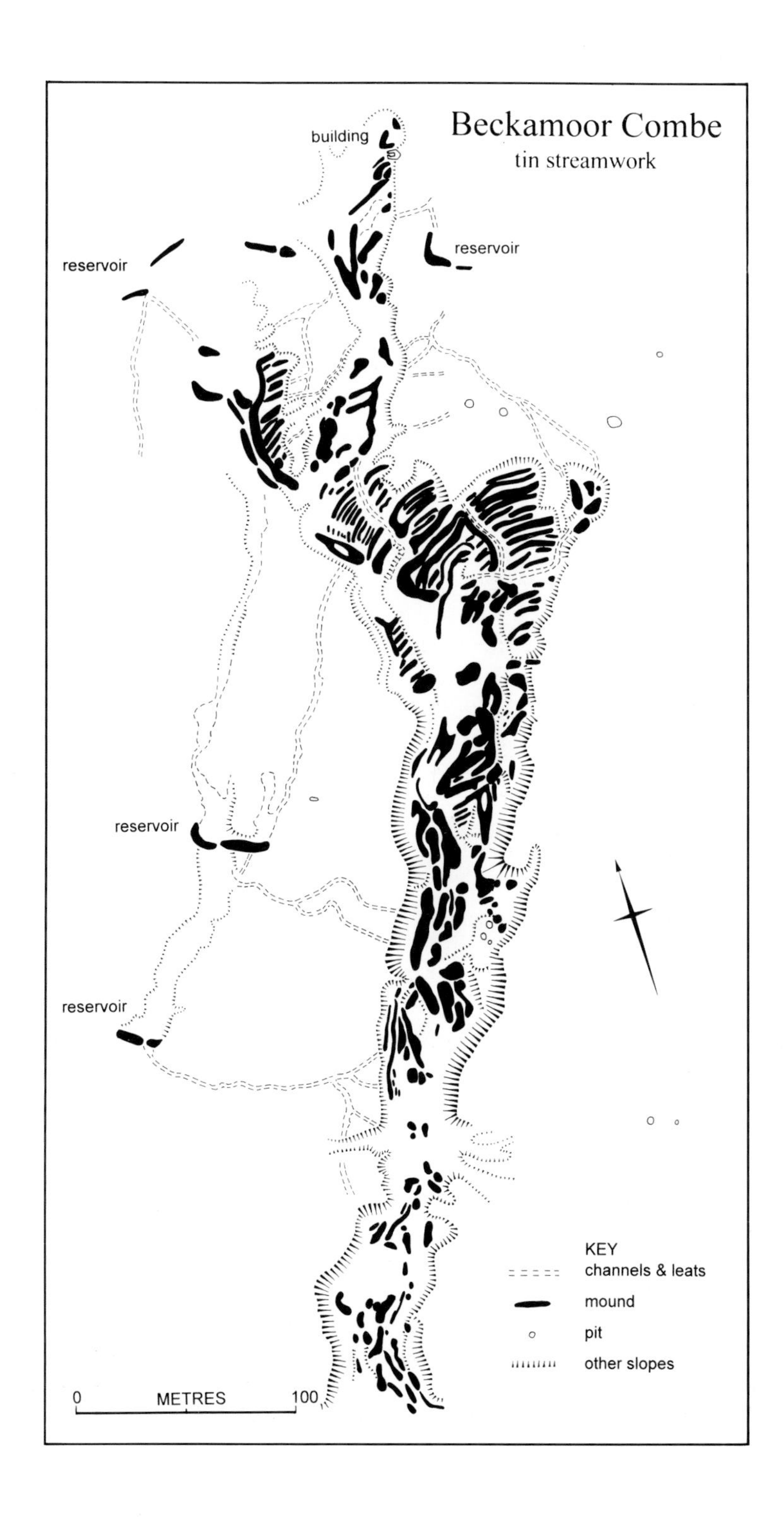
Beckamoor Combe
tin streamwork
building
reservoir
reservoir
reservoir
reservoir
KEY
channels & leats
mound
pit
other slopes
0
METRES
100

can be up to 5m deep, such as is found at the head of Western Wella Brook or along the East Okement. These scarps are however, just as commonly only of very slight proportions if the deposit was shallow as it was at locations like Sunshine Valley near Swincombe Head.

The interior of the tinwork comprises a series of linear mounds of rubble, accompanied by networks of water channels. The mounds have often become covered by turf since their abandonment while the channels, now dry and silted, may support moisture loving plants such as rushes. At a first glance these features appear to be placed haphazardly but careful examination can often reveal that the exploitation of an area was indeed very systematic at some streamworks.

The remains conform to a number of different types, each reflecting differing techniques. The technique used would have depended on the nature of the deposit, the local topography and to some extent the preferences of the individual tinners involved. The most common type of streamwork consists of linear banks of stones and waste arranged in parallel groups. The orientation and positioning of these sets of banks will vary depending on the unique characteristics of each tin deposit, but they may be aligned coaxially with the prevailing alignment of the working itself, or curving obliquely into the outer edge of the streamwork. Often several different arrangements exist within a single tinwork, suggesting different episodes of work or different requirements dictated by separate areas of the deposit. The channels or *tyes* represent the working area through which water passed, to separate out the finer waste then washing it away. William Pryce mentions the use of an inclined timber board on which to do this within the tye. The cassiterite could then be sorted and removed while the larger waste was shovelled onto spoil dumps running parallel with the water channel. As work progressed further, generally in an uphill direction, new tyes were begun, parallel with the first and the spoil from each new tye could then be dumped into the channel of its predecessor. The resulting remains, after the process has been repeated several times, are the parallel banks of spoil which we see today. The channel of the tye is not always visible where it has been buried beneath the dumps, though the final tye, before work ceased, usually remains. Some very clear parallel banks are to be seen at Ivytor Water

Plate 1(Top). Aerial view of the tin streamworks along the River Swincombe, near Foxtor, showing the parallel banks of spoil running both obliquely across, and coaxial with, the axis of the working (SX 635 702). (Photo. F. M. Griffith, Devon County Council, 12/1/88: copyright reserved)

Plate2(Lower). Stone reveted tyes in the Dry Lake tin streamwork in the O Brook Valley (SX 661 705).

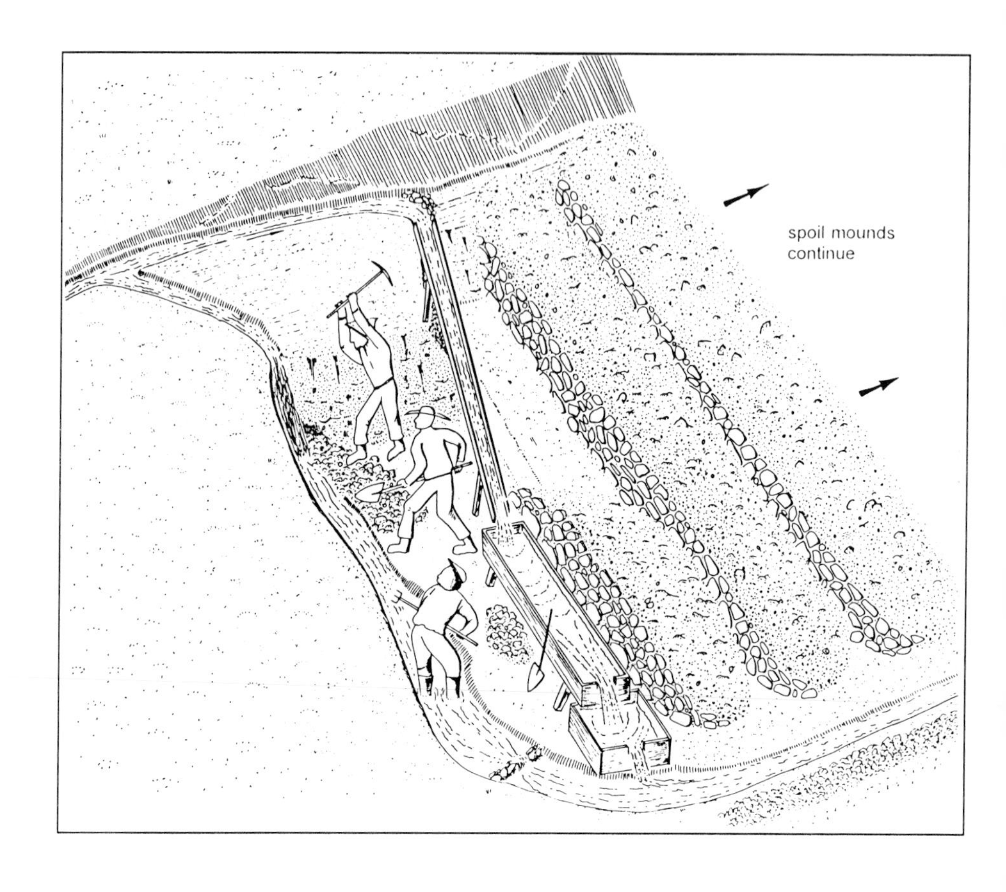

Fig. 5. Visualisation of tin streaming method, based on information from Hitchens & Drew (1824), William Pryce (1778) and Agricola (1556). The drawing shows a parallel dump type streamwork (see page 16) remains of which are common over much of Dartmoor at both alluvial and eluvial workings. The dumps may be set obliquely or at right angles to the prevailing axis of the working (as illustrated) or may be coaxial to the working itself. Examples of the former may be seen at Lower Dry Lake (SX 665 710) and Brim Brook (SX 588 872), while the latter survive at Swincombe (SX 635 702) (Plate 1). The dry-stone revetment or 'stilling' was not used at all streamworks or in some cases may not be visible: good examples may be seen at Lower Dry Lake and Ducks Pool (SX 627 678).

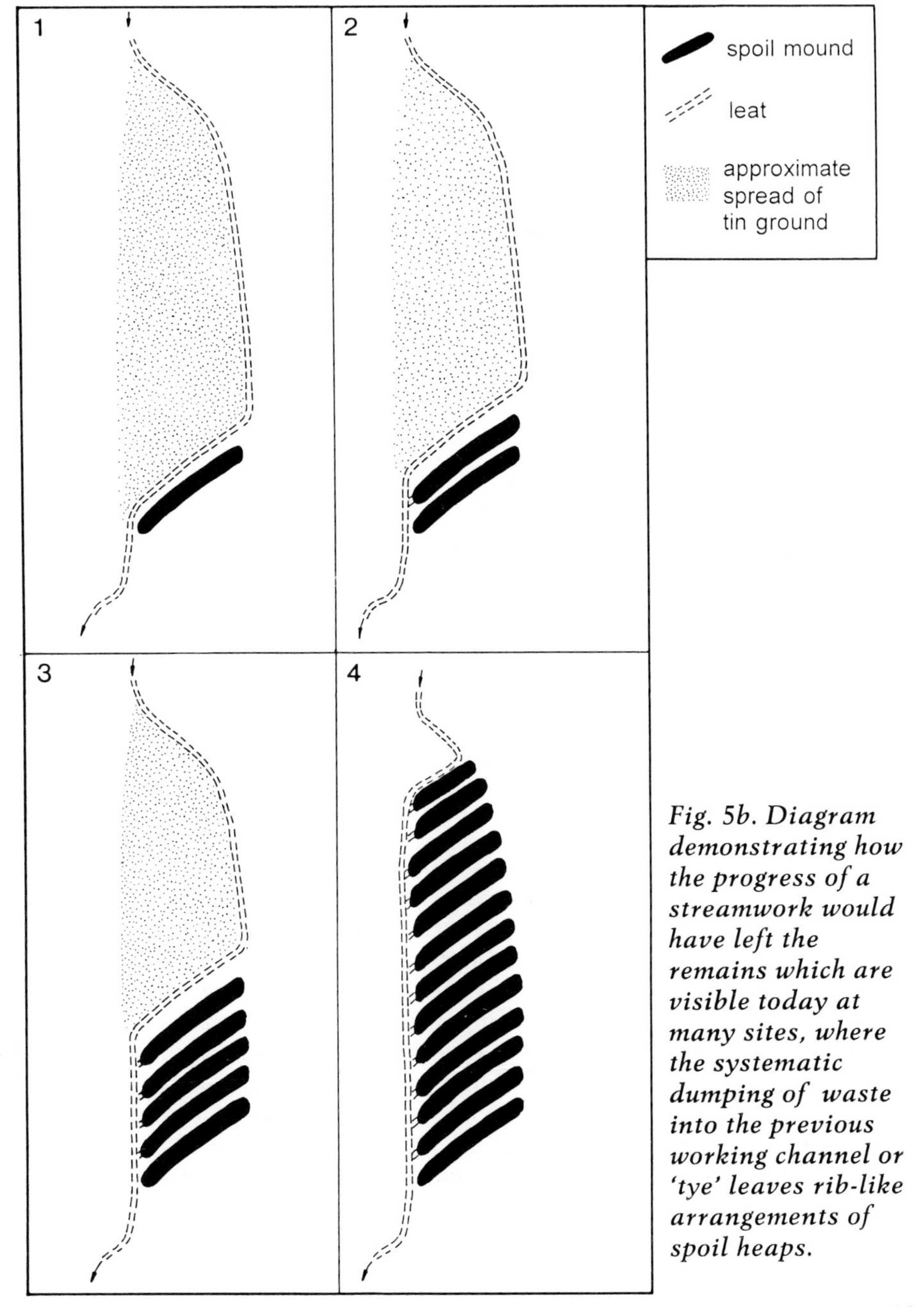

Fig. 5b. Diagram demonstrating how the progress of a streamwork would have left the remains which are visible today at many sites, where the systematic dumping of waste into the previous working channel or 'tye' leaves rib-like arrangements of spoil heaps.

and others exist on the O Brook, Brim Brook, Langcombe Brook and Walla Brook.

At several locations the front face of the tye, called the stilling by Hitchens and Drew, consists of a well-built dry-stone revetment, constructed from larger boulders, behind which smaller pieces of rubble are retained. Probably the best known example of this is at Duck's Pool Stream but others exist at Dry Lake (Plate 2) and they occur at many other places. At some streamworks, such as those in the lower valley floor of Newleycombe Lake, the system of work is not so readily identified from the field remains, and certainly appear to be the result of random digging and piling up of spoil. The working of these sites was undoubtedly systematic at the time of the activity, but the remains today just do not lend themselves to easy interpretation of the techniques used. It is also often the case that later reworking of an abandoned tinwork would result in disturbance of the earlier evidence. Occasionally the interior of the streamwork will contain large areas which are devoid of any mounds at all, the section of Beckamoor Combe south of the road has patches like this. These areas may have contained little in the way of larger waste stones, and the waste that was present was small enough to be swept away by the action of the water.

A detailed study of Cornish streamworks by Gerrard[7] resulted in the identification of a number of variations on the basic streamwork field remains, suggesting the use of several different methods. No such study has yet been undertaken on Dartmoor though it is likely that similar observations would result.

Water supplies to the streamworks would usually have come from the nearest stream or river, which in the case of most alluvial workings would be that under which the deposit has formed. Where the supply was plentiful, only short diversions would have been needed, via channels contained within what became the working area, often destroyed by later progress at the tinwork. At some streamworks, short sections of these channels may be seen skirting the outer edges of the working, created to divert water from higher up river to a lower section of the working within the same alluvial plane. Examples of this may be seen along the east side of the East Okement and along the east side of the North Teign. Occasionally the on-site water supply was supplemented by an additional source if the natural supply was insufficient, and to do this artificial water courses or leats were dug to bring water in from elsewhere. The massive streamwork on the East Okement at Skit Bottom for example, part of a working which extends from the head of the river for over 4km north to Hartor Farm, although today possessing a respectable flow of water from the East Okement itself, also had a supply diverted from the adjacent Taw River Valley, over a distance of 2.5km. The shallow earthwork channel of the leat is visible over most of its course, running along the west side of the Taw Valley and crossing the top of Oke Tor Ridge.

Some streamworks are so located that they had either a very limited natural water supply available, or none at all. These usually exploited a slightly different form of deposit known as *eluvial*. Although weathered from the parent lodes in the same way, the final deposition differed in as much as they were not carried to the valley floors by alluvial action and did not benefit from the sorting action that would incur. They are usually found extending up gently sloping hillsides, or in shallow combes away from the river. Water would be either diverted to the works via leats tapping the nearest river source, or, where the working was situated above such supplies, then rainwater was collected in shallow channels constructed along the hillside above the working. Being so sporadic the available water needed to be stored and small reservoirs were constructed above the working areas in which water would be allowed to accumulate, to be used as required.

The reservoirs consist of hollows dug into the hillside with an earth and stone retaining bank on the downslope side. The bank may be straight, with an opening at one end, or crescentic with curving banks and a central opening, though several less common variants also exist. Recorded examples are between 13m and 70m long[8], and may be up to 2m high. A masonry lining may often be seen on either side of the opening which represents the surviving components of the sluice.

Typical examples of streamworks with associated water systems may be seen in the valley of Newleycombe Lake and the finest of these lies just to the east of Classiwell Farm, extending up the hillside. Three very fine reservoirs survive at the head of the tinwork. Others are to be seen further down the hill, close to the western outer scarp. A leat may also be traced from the top reservoirs, around the western knoll of Raddick Hill and up to the head of Hartor Brook, from which water was diverted. Another streamwork with well-preserved reservoirs, is Beckamoor Combe (Fig. 4). Two survive to the west of the tinwork, with clear leat channels leading off into the working area. The source was the hillside run-off from Cox Tor. A further very fine example may be seen to the south-east of Dry Lake on Holne Moor.

LODE WORKINGS

Not all Dartmoor's tin lodes had been broken down by weathering and alluvial action to be exploited by tinners in rich streamworks. Many lodes remained where they had originally been formed, and were probably an untapped source of tin until late medieval times. With so many rich sources of stream tin available before then it seems extremely unlikely that any attention was paid to the lodes, which were by comparison less accessible and demanded greater effort, in both extraction and refining. However, such was the demand for and value of tin that by the 15th century the working of lodes was considered viable and their exploitation was beginning.

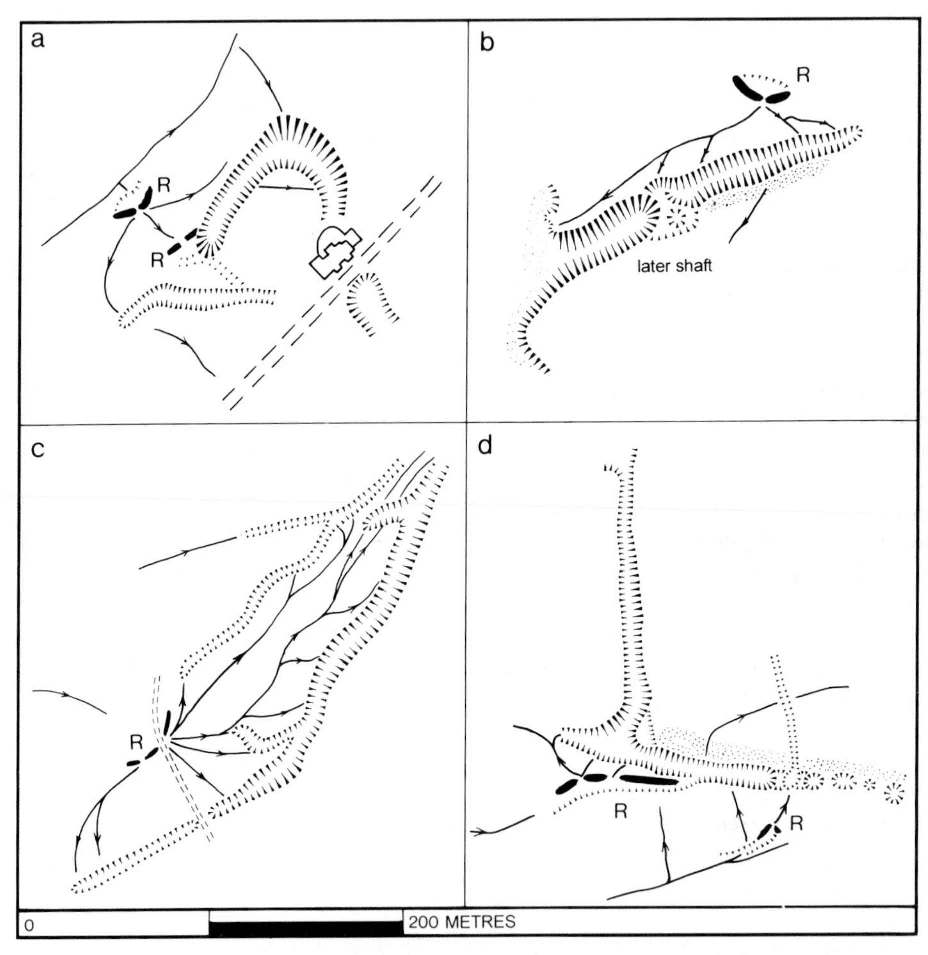

Fig. 6. Simplified plans of individual openworks and their water supplies: a) Warren House Inn - SX 674 810; b) Crane Lake - SX 608 684; c) Bush Down - SX 676 813; d) Ringleshuttes - SX 6775 6975. All of these examples demonstrate clearly their supply of water but are also each only one element of much larger tinworking landscapes. Key: solid lines show leats with direction of flow; R = reservoir dam.

The most conspicuous remains of lode working used by the earlier tinners are openworks. By this method the lode was worked by digging down from the surface, rather than mining from below, and the resulting field remains are the massive open gullies, of which those at Birch Tor (Fig. 8; Plate 3), Ringleshuttes(Fig. 7) and Henroost are spectacular examples. The tinners referred to this type of working as 'beamworks' and several have the word 'beam' as part of their name, such as Willabeam, Scudley Beam and Gibby Beam. The term 'gert' has also been applied in more recent literature. A second method of exploiting lodes was the 'lodeback work' or 'lodeback pits' where a series of pits was dug down from above onto the backs of the lodes. It is possible that lodeback works were often a precursor to the openworks, and the latter technique was adopted at sites where greater depth was needed, but many lodeback works survive as testament to this being a separate technique in its own right.

One study, investigating the documentation of part of south-west Dartmoor has revealed that many of the openworks in that area may be assigned to a period of between the 15th and 17th century, though one or two less certain examples could well be slightly earlier[9]. However, this could be misleading as early documents (i.e. pre-1500) are rare for all categories of tinwork and some of the larger workings of this type, such as Ringleshuttes, Henroost, and Birch Tor have no known documentation surviving, so we cannot at present be more precise with dating. We should certainly keep an open mind regarding the possibility of pre-1500 openworks. Similarly, there is unlikely to be an identifiable date when the technique ceased to be used, as the transition from it to underground mining was probably gradual, but by 1778 when Pryce wrote his comprehensive description of the Cornish tin industry, openworking was clearly considered an antiquated method as he writes:

> *I do not suppose the present methods for working of tin mines, by deep Shafts, and by Driving and Stopeing under the firm ground, has been practiced more than 3 hundred years past. Prior to those means for raising of tin, they wrought a Vein from the bryle to a depth of 8 or 10 fathoms, all open to grass, very much like the fosse of an entrenchment*[10].

The same could very likely have been so for Devon as well.

As yet there are few documentary references which may be confidently assigned specifically to a lodeback work, though there are several possibilities. These include Great Hingston mentioned 1611[11], where a line of deep pits remain in a field of that name, and Holming Beam[12] where a spectacular line of lodeback pits is to be found, though the only records for the latter are of the 19th century.

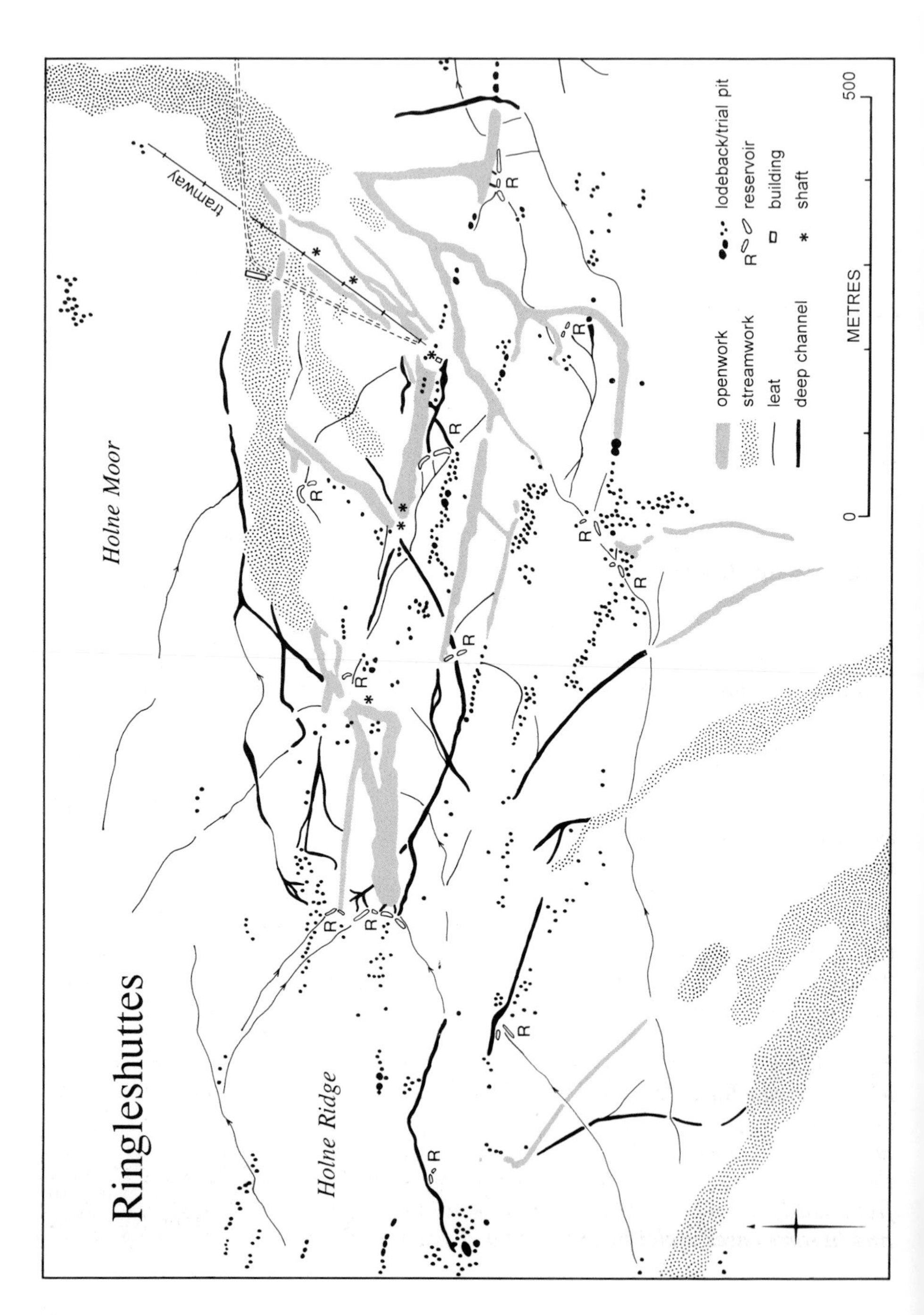
Ringleshuttes
Holne Moor
Holne Ridge
tramway
openwork
streamwork
leat
deep channel
lodeback/trial pit
R reservoir
building
shaft
0
500
METRES
R

The methods of prospecting used to locate the lodes were described by several contemporary writers, including Pryce in 1778, who had great faith in the use of the divining rod. He also described a method known as 'costeening' which consisted of digging rows of three or four pits across the line of a suspected lode, in the hope of finding samples of tin bearing deposits called shode[13]. These are fragments of vein material which had become detached by weathering and had undergone a certain amount of transportation, away from the parent lode. The greater the concentration of shode they found the nearer they were to a vein and the process was repeated until the lode was discovered. If however, after several rows of pits, dug progressively higher up the hillside, proved to be devoid of tin, then work was abandoned. Much of the skill must have lain in knowing the type of place to look to begin with.

An anonymous writer of 1670 also describes this technique of digging what he calls 'essay hatches' which literally translated we may take to mean test or trial pits.

For in the next place we sink down about the foot or bottom of the Hill an Essay hatch (an oriface made for the search of a vein, about 6 foot long and four foot broad) as deep as the shelf... Albeit we find no Shoad in this first Hatch. we are not (as yet) altogether discouraged but ascend commonly about 12 fathoms and sink a 2d Hatch... till we come to the top of the hill, and if we find none in any of these Hatches, then farewell to that Hill[14].

Trial pits may be seen at many locations on Dartmoor though naturally at the site of a successful prospecting stage, many of the pits would have been effaced by the subsequent working activity. At unpromising trials the pits remain visible as small clusters or lines of conical hollows, up to 3m diameter with a crescentic ring of spoil on the downslope side.

Once successfully located, the business of exploiting the ore source probably began by the digging of a series of larger pits down onto the lode and raising the tin up to the surface in buckets. The lines of confluent, staggered pairs of 'lodeback' pits, which may be seen running up or across the sides of a hill, are the evidence of this activity, though are easily confused with trial pits, especially

Fig. 7. Openworks and their associated water systems in the area of Ringleshuttes Mine on Holne Ridge (centred SX 6750 6980). This remarkable tinworking landscape has seen intense periods of streamworking and underground mining but it is most notable for the extent and survival of the opencast lode workings, or openworks, and the many leats, water channels and reservoirs which supplied the site with water from mostly rainwater sources. Note also the many pits in the area, prospecting for and in some cases exploiting, sections of lode (after RCHME, ©Crown Copyright).

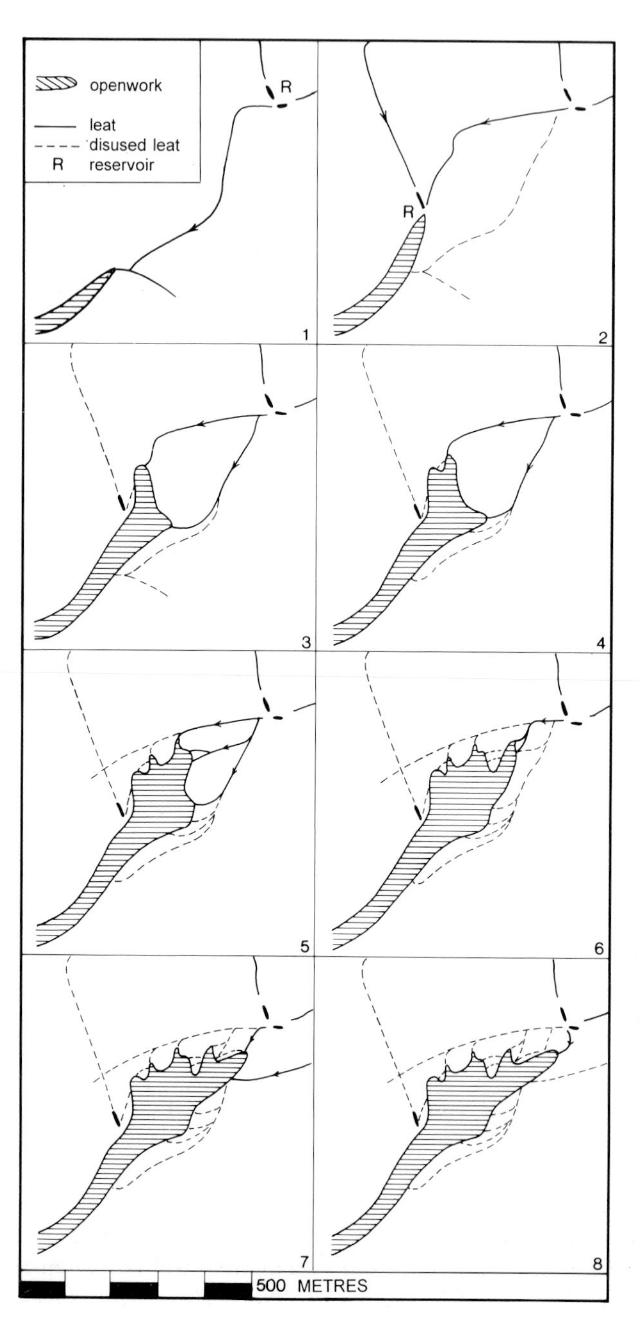

Fig. 8. Frame diagram demonstrating the probable stages in the expansion of an openwork at Birch Tor (SX 6825 8135). Showing how new water supplies needed to be established as work progressed up the hill. The phases are all based on surviving evidence, though the scheme as a whole does not include the use of the main water supplies at other nearby openworks which is a further possibility. There would also have been many intermediate phases which we are unable to determine from the surviving evidence.

where the two occur together, although trial pits are normally smaller and often traverse the lode whereas the lodeback pits are coaxial to the lode. Many examples of lodeback pits may be seen in the valleys of Newleycombe Lake and Hartor Brook on south-west Dartmoor, though they are extremely common over most of the high moors. These are not in the true sense shafts as they probably did not penetrate the ground to any great depth, but rather until safety prevented them proceeding any deeper for fear of the sides falling in, though it is likely that the pits did interconnect below ground and some shoring could have been used.

Many lode works would undoubtedly have held greater promise than this technique was suitable for and they developed into the much bigger openworks. These works allowed the ore to be chased to greater depths, but to do so it was necessary to remove the ground surrounding it to gain access. This was probably done initially with picks and shovels to loosen the overburden, which was in most cases a soft, crumbly growan. A fast flow of water could then be used to wash away this unwanted material, rather than manhandling it, leaving the tin-bearing rocks, exposed to be removed and taken elsewhere for crushing and processing.

Openworks consist of linear or curving, steep-sided gullies which may be up to 450m long by a maximum of 40m wide and up to 20m deep, though most are much smaller. The secondary element always associated with openworks, is the systems of collecting, diverting and storing water. In a way similar to the streamworks, leats fed by rivers or rainwater run-off, delivered water to the working and reservoirs retained the water prior to it being used.

The water systems which supplied the openworks were, like those to the streamworks, clearly of fundamental importance to the process as every such working has one to a greater or lesser extent. At some sites several kilometres of leat provided water from far off and often meagre sources, to be collected in small reservoirs above the working area. Complex systems of reservoirs and distribution channels may be found around some of the workings, while others consisted of a single reservoir sited above the openwork, as at Crane Lake (Fig. 6d). The finest surviving reservoir associated with an openwork may be seen at Henroost, to the south of the working. It has an exceptionally well-preserved sluice opening, made from large upright slabs of granite and a retaining bank or 'dam' still standing to 1.5m high. It is one of several which stored water for use in this tinwork.

One 17th-century Cornish writer referred to the use of streams of water diverted along the hill contours and released in torrents down the hillsides of Cornwall as a method of prospecting for tin, where soil and overburden were washed away, hopefully leaving the lode exposed.[15] This method is known as 'hushing' in the lead bearing districts of England and Wales, where it was used widely. If used on Dartmoor we would expect to find the remains of unsuccessful attempts at hushing but there is little evidence for this and it is more likely that water supplies to openworks were purely part of the extraction process rather than being used for prospecting.

Several documents and bibliographical references imply that much of the waste from openworks and streamworks was dispersed by disposing of it in the nearest river. In 1532 for example, prompted by the inhabitants of Plymouth and Dartmouth fearing the silting of their harbours, the Stannary Parliament ordained that:

> *..every Person or Persons that hereafter shall Work in any Stream Works, or cause any Stream Work to be Wrought, that they and every of them Convey and Carry, or cause to be conveyed and carried, the Gravel, Ruble and Sands, into old Hatches, Tipittes, miry places, or other convenient places, from the said great Rivers, so that the said Gravel, Ruble or Sands be not conveyed to the said Havens of Dartmouth and Plimouth..*[16]

and in 1638 tinworking is implicated in the silting problems at Catwater Harbour, Plymouth:

> *..harbor is of late years much decayed and quared up with gravell, sand and stones and ballast which appeared playnly to be occasioned by the great quantity of sand and earth which dyvers tynners working in a Tynneworkes called Clasiewell and other works and Tynne Milles neare the rivers of Plym and Mewe, which fall into the said harbour convey out of their said works and Mylles into the said rivers*[17].

Clasiwell is a particularly large openwork, on south-west Dartmoor, now filled with water and referred to on modern maps as Crazy Well Pool and though unlikely to be solely responsible for the problem, it is clear that tinworking generally was seen as a major contributor to harbour silting.

This problem of waste silts was clearly an unavoidable part of the process in a streamwork, where the temptation to dump it into the moving water of the river must have been irresistible. However, a recent experimental excavation of Lydford Woods streamwork by Sandy Gerrard[18] has demonstrated that some waste silts were dumped into disused areas of the working in an attempt to dispose of the material more responsibly. It is less clear exactly how dumping in the river would have happened in openworks, where parts of the working may be several hundred metres from the river, considering also the limitations of the artificial water supply, which would not necessarily have carried the waste all the way down to the river. However, there is always less spoil than we would

Plate 3. View looking south-east across the massive openworks of Chaw Gully, part of the Birch Tor and Vitifer complex (SX 688 808).

anticipate associated with openworks and which we might expect to have accumulated at the lower end of, or outside the working, had it not been somehow disposed of.

Three important areas of Dartmoor, demonstrate the physical remains left by the working of tin lodes particularly well. At Ringleshuttes (Fig. 7) a complex and impressive system of deep openworks was supported by a labyrinth of water channels, which due to the altitude utilised mostly hillside run-off sources. Henroost, only 1.5km north-west of Ringleshuttes, has an impressive rock-cut openwork and a well-preserved set of reservoirs. However, the area known generally as Birch Tor and Vitifer mines, is the most accessible and has the highest concentration of openworks in a single area, accompanied by a complex system of leats which exploited a variety of water supplies in the area.

When the Dartmoor tin industry fell into decline in the early 17th century, it is likely that the techniques of streamworking and of working lodes in the ways described above, were on their way to becoming obsolete. Rich alluvial deposits had been worked to near exhaustion, and the working of lodes on such a scale had probably become uneconomic. When a brief, and somewhat small scale revival of the industry's fortunes came about in the late 18th and 19th centuries, the technology had moved on and much of the search for tin went underground, exploiting lodes at deeper levels and taking advantage of explosives and pumping machinery which made this possible. These and other aspects of later mining are discussed in chapter 5.

Grid refs for examples in chapter 2

Beckamoor Combe	SX 5350 7500
Birch Tor	SX 6800 8100 (centred)
Brim Brook	SX 5880 8720
Classiwell	SX 5820 7048
Crane Lake	SX 6080 6845
Dry Lake	SX 6610 7050
Duck's Pool	SX 6270 6780
East Okement	SX 6070 9060
Gibby Beam	SX 6680 6783
Great Hingston	SX 5832 6912
Hartor Brook	SX 5800 7150
Henroost	SX 6515 7112
Holming Beam	SX 5826 7645
Ivy Tor Water	SX 6290 9160
Langcombe Brook	SX 6040 6700
Newleycombe Lake	SX 5860 7040 (eluvial workings)
Newleycombe Lake	SX 5840 6985 (alluvial workings)
North Teign	SX 6428 8668
O Brook	SX 6500 7132 (centred)
Ringleshuttes	SX 6750 6980 (centred)
Scudley Beam	SX 6920 8020
Skit Bottom	SX 6070 8980
Skir Gut	SX 6472 7040
Sunshine Valley	SX 6330 6970
Taw Marsh	SX 6160 9070
Walla Brook	SX 6740 8030
Western Wella Brook	SX 6650 6850
West Okement	SX 5780 8720
Willabeam	SX 5934 7015

References

1 Claughton 1996, 35
2 De La Beche 1839, 399
3 Chope 1918
4 Risdon 1714
5 Pryce 1778, 133
6 Hitchens & Drew 1824, 603-4
7 Gerrard 1987, 7-3
8 Newman 1987, 232-3
9 Greeves 1987a, 239-40
10 Pryce 1778, 141
11 Newman 1994, 227
12 Greeves 1981, 325
13 Pryce 1778, 124
14 Anon 1670- quoted in Greeves 1981, 124
15 ibid, 125
16 Radford 1930, 239
17 W.S.B.H. 1922-3, 238-9
18 Gerrard 1997b

3

Tin Mills

Once removed from the ground, tin ore needs to undergo a complex series of processes, including crushing, refining and smelting, before becoming a usable commodity. In the earliest days of the tin industry on Dartmoor, the rich and easily accessible alluvial gravels provided a very pure form of ore. These gravels would need a minimum of crushing, if any, before being smelted in small, outdoor furnaces, probably very near the tinworking site, leaving an imperceivable level of archaeological evidence. By late medieval times, the economic benefit of high tin production, brought with it the need to exploit less rich deposits, intensifying the effort involved in tin processing, especially crushing. This in turn led to a degree of mechanisation for both crushing and smelting and from about the mid 14th century onwards, most of these processes were carried out in small mills.

Structural remains from over 50 tin mills survive on Dartmoor as well as a further 30 sites where artefacts or other evidence indicate the former location of a mill. This represents a remarkable survival rate for Devon tin mills, especially compared with Cornwall where despite the far higher level of tin production and known documentation for a great many mills, there is surprisingly only a small handful of sites where field evidence has been recorded[1].

Tin mills are roughly rectangular buildings, within which the tin processing machinery was housed, powered by a waterwheel. The walls are always of a dry-stone construction, using unhewn or roughly dressed moorstone, built randomly or sometimes in approximate courses. Their condition today varies greatly between the well-preserved, extant walls at Week Ford(Fig 9c), and the mostly destroyed building at Gobbett, now recognisable mainly by stone artefacts visible there (Plates 12 & 13). Others mills, such as one example in the Plym Valley (Fig 13c), are completely covered by turf and survive as little more than an earthwork. The interior dimensions of the mills varies between 9.8m by 4.7m at a large mill, such as Middle Merrivale(Fig 9a), and the small Plym mill already mentioned, which is only 2.5m by 4.5m.

The mills are most commonly sited close to a stream and built into the base of the natural, or sometimes artificial, slope which forms the edge of a river valley.

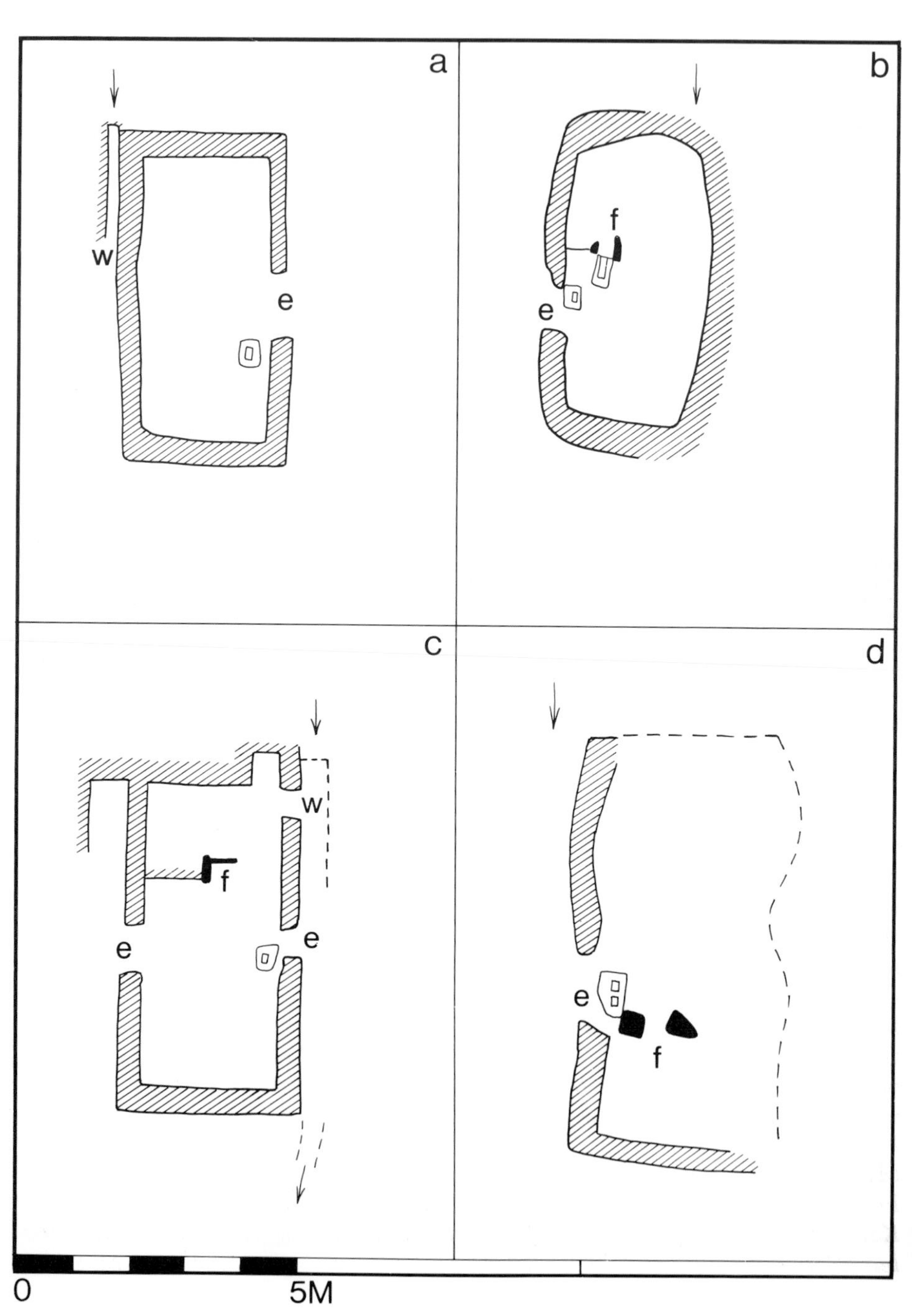
a
w
e
b
f
e
c
w
f
e
e
d
e
f
0
5M

Plate 4. One of the best preserved tin mill structures may be seen on the left bank of the River Meavy at Black Tor Falls (SX 57487161) The walls remain to a good height and the clear entrance has its lintel still in place (see also Fig. 13a).

This would provide a sufficient drop in height for water, diverted from the stream via a leat, to be delivered onto the top of the waterwheel, using either an overshot or pitchback arrangement. These were probably the only types used in the Dartmoor tin mill where water supplies, though reliable, could not supply the volume necessary for an undershot wheel. Waterwheels were usually housed in narrow stone wheelpits attached to the exterior of the main mill structure or, more rarely, could be contained within the mill building. Examples of the former are Upper and Middle Merrivale(Fig 9a; 10) and Colesmill (Fig 13b) on the River Plym, while the latter may be seen at the Taw River mill. R. H. Worth who compiled statistics based on his research, was able to suggest that the

Fig. 9. Simplified ground plans of blowing mill structures: a) Middle Merrivale (SX 5527 7624); b) Lower Merrivale (SX 5526 7534); c) Week Ford (SX 6618 7232); d) Blacksmith's Shop (SX 6377 8426).
Key: e = entrance; w = wheelpit; f = furnace. Arrow indicates flow of water from leat. Note position of mouldstones adjacent to the entrances in all four examples.

Plate 5. Remains of a wheelpit on the tin stamping mill at Colesmill, Plym (SX59356676). Note the mortarstone on the right-hand side of the wheelpit which has been reused as an axle bearing stone.

average waterwheel was of 9ft 3"(2.8m) diameter, with the largest being 10ft(3m) and the smallest 8ft(2.5m), with a breast of between 1ft 6"(46cm) and 2ft(60cm).[2]

Water was conducted from the leat onto the wheel via a wooden channel or launder. In a well-positioned mill, at the foot of a steep slope, the launder would be fairly short, as for example at the Nosworthy left bank mill, where there is a drop of about 3m from the leat to the wheelpit. When at the foot of a more gentle gradient, a wedge shaped embankment was built above the mill, coaxial with the wheelpit, over which the final section of leat was diverted. A very fine leat embankment of this type survives at Colesmill.

Power from the waterwheel was transmitted to the machinery inside the building by means of a drive shaft which passed through an aperture in the wall adjacent to the wheelpit. At Broad Falls and at Week Ford lower mill these roughly square apertures, capped by lintels have survived.

The waterwheels, drive shafts and any other rotating components were supported using iron axles, bedded into primitive stone bearings. These are semi-circular polished slots usually about 20-30mm diameter by approximately 50-90mm long on the face of a granite stone. The polishing was caused by wear resulting from an iron axle rotating in the slot. The adjacent sides of the stone will often have concentric, arc-shaped wear marks, suggesting that a larger rotating component, such as the waterwheel itself perhaps, was rubbing the stone. At the Nosworthy left bank mill, several examples of these bearings may be seen and also at Upper Merrivale where fresh examples have come to light as a result of the archaeological excavations. At Colesmill (Plate 5), the bearing stone of the waterwheel is still in-situ on the edge of the wheelpit, utilising a previously discarded mortarstone (see also Plate 9). Not all waterwheels used these primitive bearings, for there is evidence that 'plumber block' bearings were used as well. In this case a small rectangle was cut into the supporting stones into which an iron bearing could be set. One such stone may be seen *in situ* in one side of the Nosworthy left bank wheelpit and another was recovered from the wheelpit at Upper Merrivale. It is likely that these bearings are a later innovation.

No windows have survived in tin mills but several mills have well preserved entrances. At Black Tor Falls for example(Plate 4), the granite lintel above the door is still in place and the uprights of the door lining have vertical grooves cut into them to accommodate the woodwork of the door jambs, as well as slots and holes for iron fittings and hinges.

Tin mills fall broadly into two categories - blowing and stamping. Blowing mills or blowing houses contained small blast furnaces for which a forced

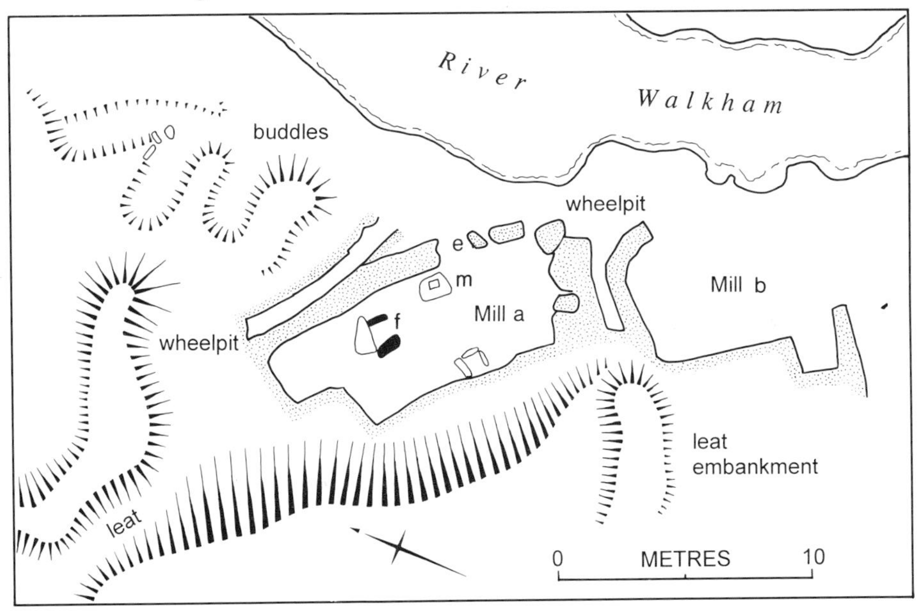

Fig. 10. Simplified earthwork plan of Upper Merrivale mill (SX 5519 7664) which was archaeologically excavated by the Dartmoor Tinworking Research Group between 1991-96. There are two mills at the site, both built into the foot of a steep slope near the river's edge. Mill 'a' demonstrates well the layout of a blowing mill with an external wheelpit, the mouldstone (m) sited near the entrance (e) [see also Fig. 9 a-d] and a furnace (f) within the building. Only surviving walls are illustrated (after Gerrard & Greeves 1992).

draught was supplied by waterwheel-powered bellows, and where prepared cassiterite was smelted and cast into ingots. The cassiterite was prepared for smelting in stamping mills or 'knacking/knocking' mills. The stamping mill contained mechanical crushing equipment, activated by a waterwheel. Some mills have evidence of both blowing and stamping though we can never be certain that both were occurring simultaneously. It is often more likely that two phases of separate activity at the same site are represented by the different evidence.

BLOWING MILLS

The first tin blowing mills may have existed on Dartmoor as early as the 14th century. Before then the limitations of the technology had made it necessary for tin to be smelted twice. After a first smelting which may well have taken place at or near the site of the tinwork, the roughly smelted tin was taken to a Stannary town for a second smelting to produce a more refined product. A tax payable at a rate of 30d per thousandweight on the first smelt was supplemented in 1198 by an additional 13s 4d per thousandweight at the second smelting.[3] However, probably as a result of improved technology which allowed smelting to be achieved in a single process, both taxes were replaced by a single tax of 1s 6¾d per hundredweight on the finished tin in 1303. It is likely that the blowing mill was developed during this period and was an integral part of this transition.

Although documentation confirms the existence of tin blowing mills in Cornwall as early as 1402[4], on Dartmoor it is not until the early 16th century that the first documented blowing mills are mentioned. At Dartmeet for example a 'blowyng mill' had recently been built in 1514[5](Fig. 2). However, this lack of earlier references is more likely to be due to poor survival of documents and it is highly probable that blowing mills had been at work on Dartmoor for quite some time before this. We have many more references to blowing mills from the 16th and 17th century, particularly the first half of the 16th when the industry was enjoying something of a mini-boom[6]. Nevertheless, by 1730 only two blowing mills were operating in Devon at Sheepstor and at Plympton[7]. These two may reflect a short period of prosperity for the industry which is recorded in the late 17th and early 18th century[8] and were probably among the last smelting mills on Dartmoor to use the blast furnace.

The most commonly occurring field evidence to confirm that a tin mill was used for smelting or 'blowing' is the mouldstone(Plate 6 & 7). These are large pieces of flat-topped granite with a rectangular hollow recessed in the upper surface, into which molten tin was poured to be cast into ingots. The mouldstones vary in size and shape but needed to be fairly substantial to absorb

Plate 6 (left). Small mouldstone at Longstone Sheepstor (SX 5560 6842) with hollow for casting ingot of approximately 18cm. Scale = 30cm.

Plate 7 (right). Mouldstone at Avon Dam blowing mill (SX 6722 6553) with large hollow for ingots and three 'sample' moulds to the left. NB this mouldstone is only visible at times of extreme drought. Scale = 30cm.

the high temperatures involved in the casting. There is similar variety in the dimensions and form of the hollows which may be as large as 28cm x 39cm as at Upper Merrivale or as small as that at Longstone which measures 18cm x 18cm. The bottom surface of the hollows are often flat but can sometimes be slightly concave, which would in turn have cast a slightly convex ingot. Some mouldstones have a small groove cut into the upper lip on the narrow side of the hollow. This feature is particularly clear on the mouldstone at Upper Merrivale. R.H. Worth believed that a stick would have been rested in this groove before the molten tin was poured, leaving a hole through the finished ingot by which to lever it out and as a means of tying it to a packhorse for transportation. Exactly how the stick would have borne the temperature of molten tin at approximately 1200° c is uncertain but presumably the metal would have set sufficiently before the stick was burned. The only properly recorded find of a tin ingot from Dartmoor[9], did indeed have a hole through it in the position we would expect if this idea had been practiced.

Several mouldstones have one, or sometimes two, additional, smaller rectangular hollows on their upper surface. They measure on average, 9cm x 5cm x 1-2cm deep. These are traditionally believed to be sample moulds or 'trying' moulds for testing the purity of tin as part of the assay process. Another

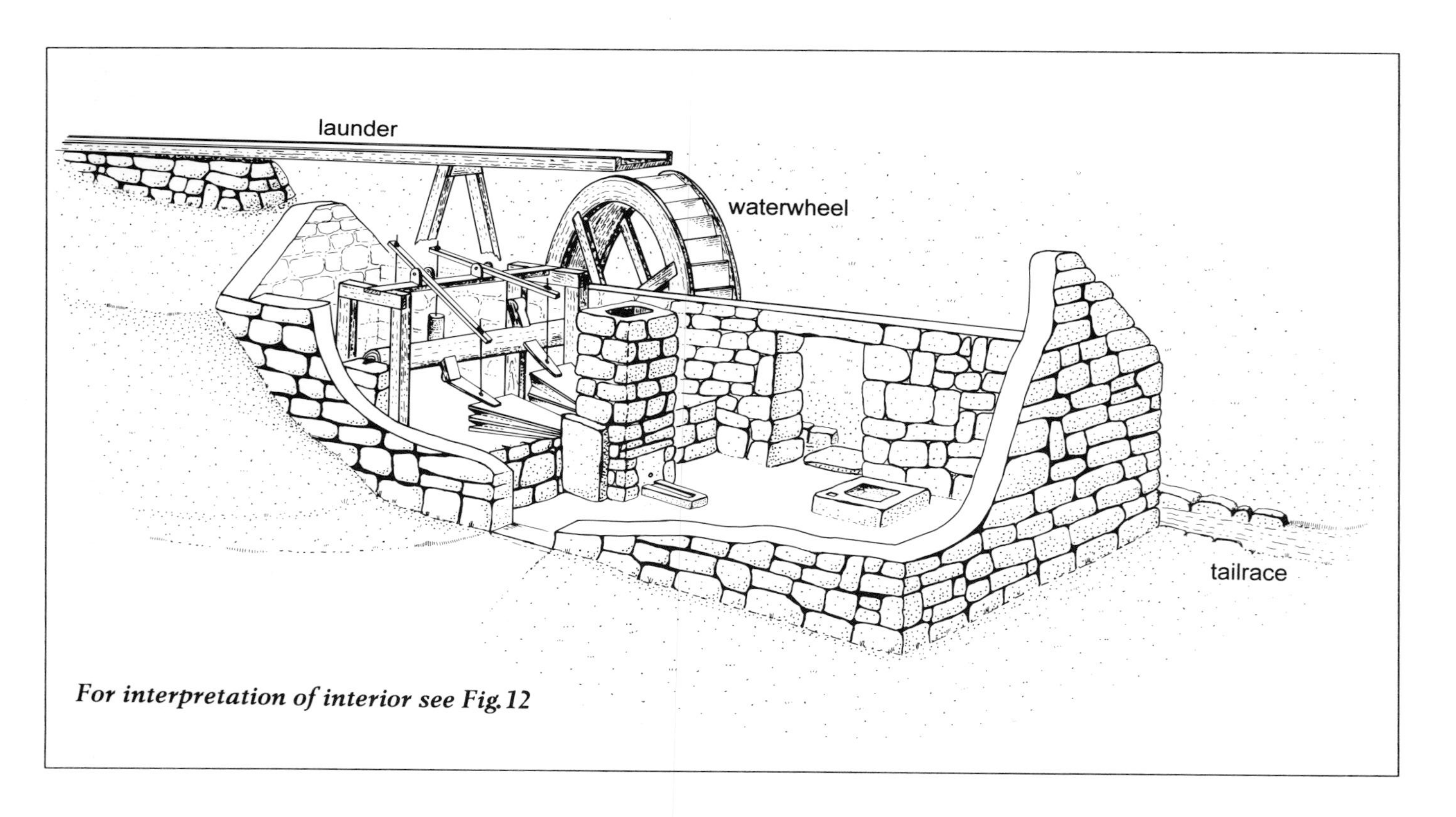

For interpretation of interior see Fig.12

possibility is that tinners would cast these small, easily concealed ingots to be sold illicitly without the knowledge of tax collectors.

All blowing mills would have housed a furnace but only a very few have survived on Dartmoor as visible field evidence. Unfortunately we have equally few descriptions of furnaces or smelting technique by contemporary writers in either Devon or Cornwall, especially for the earlier period. Thomas Beare in 1586 alluded briefly to some of the smelting practices he observed in Cornwall, mentioning some details, including the use of bellows and probably machinery to power them[10]. Also, in 1778, another Cornishman called William Pryce explained the principles of tin smelting in a forced draught furnace called a 'castle' in his treatise on Cornish mining. Although quoted several times before it is worth reproducing Pryce's description here as it is so apposite:

> *The fire place or castle, is about six feet perpendicular, two feet wide in the top part each way, and about fourteen inches in the bottom, all made of moorstone and clay, well cemented and clamped together. The pipe or nose of each bellows is fixed ten inches high from the bottom of the castle, in a large piece of wrought iron, called the Hearth-eye. The tin and charcoal are laid in the castle, stratum super stratum, in such quantities as are thought proper.*[11]

Although written some 200 years after the boom of the tin industry in Devon and probably after forced draught furnaces had mostly ceased to operate on Dartmoor, comparisons between the furnace described and surviving furnaces in Dartmoor blowing mills may certainly be made.

The field evidence for a furnace comprises two upright, roughly rectangular granite slabs, set into the ground and spaced approximately 0.5m to 0.8m apart. Such stones survive in place at Lower and Upper Merrivale, Avon Dam and Blacksmith's Shop. At Lower(Plate 8) and Upper Merrivale a further slab at the back completes what resembles an open fronted hearth. Other examples with back slabs *in situ* are lacking and we cannot assume that they were necessarily a permanent component, although the probable furnace at Week Ford also has a back slab in place. Surviving furnaces are always sited within the floor area of the mill, so that bellows could be placed behind to blow into the rear of the hearth, and are never built into the walls of the structure, as would a fireplace. Even at

Fig. 11. Reconstruction of a tin smelting or 'blowing' mill, c16th - 18th century. Not based on a particular structure but with an internal layout very similar to that of Upper Merrivale or Week Ford. Contemporary illustrations of tin smelting mills do not survive from Devon or Cornwall so the mechanisms in this case are based on examples from elsewhere in the world. For interpretation see Fig. 12.

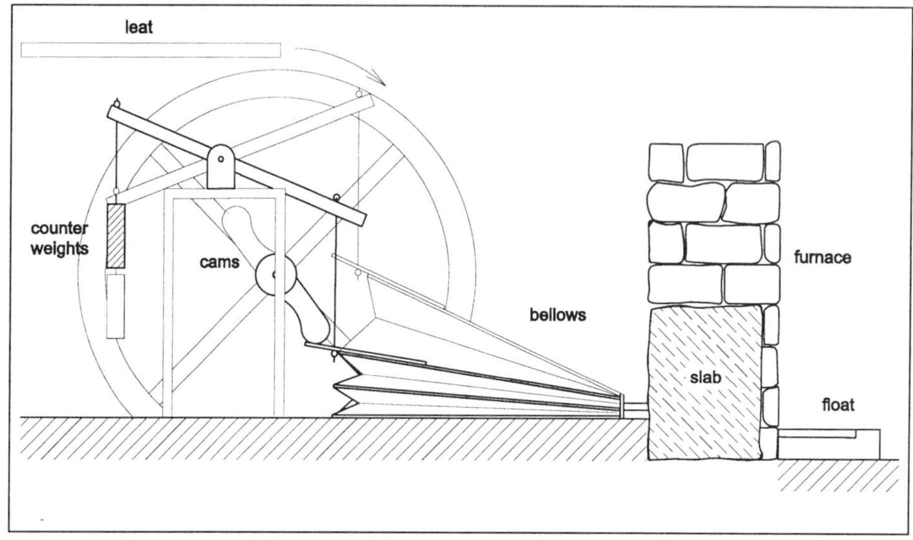

Fig. 12. Elevation of the possible interior layout of a tin blowing mill (Fig. 11) showing the position of the bellows behind the furnace, the float to the front, and a suggested method of counter-weighting the bellows.

these surviving furnaces it is clear that the remains only represent the basic shell and it is likely that the upper section of the structure was built in a less enduring manner and has since collapsed. Although some mills have what appears to be a furnace built into a wall as at Black Tor Falls right bank mill (Fig. 14), these are more likely to have served other purposes and were not used for smelting.

In the furnace, prepared cassiterite and peat charcoal which acted as a fuel and a flux were packed in, layer upon layer, as per Pryce's description. Thomas Beare, when describing a smelt of tin, seems to suggest that the furnace was heated before the tin was introduced[12]. Once alight a forced draught was created using bellows powered by the waterwheel. A single smelt was called a 'tide' and according to Thomas Beare had a duration of approximately 12 hours, during which time different types of cassiterite (usually referred to as black tin at the pre-smelting stage) were introduced in a set order, beginning with streamwork tin, followed by 'moor' tin (from lodes), then small 'myn' tin, then the waste.[13]

At Lower Merrivale mill, located within the base of the furnace is a flat-topped slab with a shallow trough, measuring 30-35cm wide by approximately 8cm deep, cut onto the upper surface. This is usually referred to as a floatstone in which molten tin would accumulate during the tide, then to be ladled into the mould. The 'flote' was also mentioned by Beare which certainly confirms it as a component of the furnace. The floatstone at Lower Merrivale and that from Longstone Sheepstor are still the only surviving examples, despite the excavations at Upper Merrivale where a furnace has been uncovered but no floatstone. When tin is smelted in a furnace, the process produces a quantity of a black glassy substance called slag, which is a waste product of the reduced ore. It often contained some unrecovered cassiterite and it was well worth the while of the smelters to collect and crush it for re-smelting. Samples of slag may often be found lying on the ground surface near tin mills. The cassiterite shows up as small pale flecks within the black matrix of the slag.

Plate 8. Furnace base at Lower Merrivale blowing mill (SX 5526 7534). The bellows would have been behind the upright slabs and the end of the float is visible in the foreground. Scale = 1m

STAMPING AND CRAZING MILLS

Before tin could be smelted, it needed to be crushed and 'dressed' to a certain standard of purity. The crushing was achieved using either stamps, which are vertically operating hammers powered by a waterwheel, or in a crazing mill where the gravels were rendered to a fine sand between two flat-faced, circular stones, the upper of which rotated. There are a least 60 buildings on Dartmoor where stamping is likely to have taken place but crazing mills are far less numerous and only three examples have been recorded.

We know from the accounts of contemporary observers, that the alluvial gravels extracted from streamworks needed little or no crushing. Any preparation which was necessary could probably be done adequately in a crazing mill. However, as these purer sources became scarcer the tinners began to exploit the courser gravels and blocky, impure lode ores which required a far higher degree of preparation including thorough crushing. This could have been done by hand using hammers in the early days but to produce crushed ore in any volume, some mechanisation was essential and the stamping mill developed as

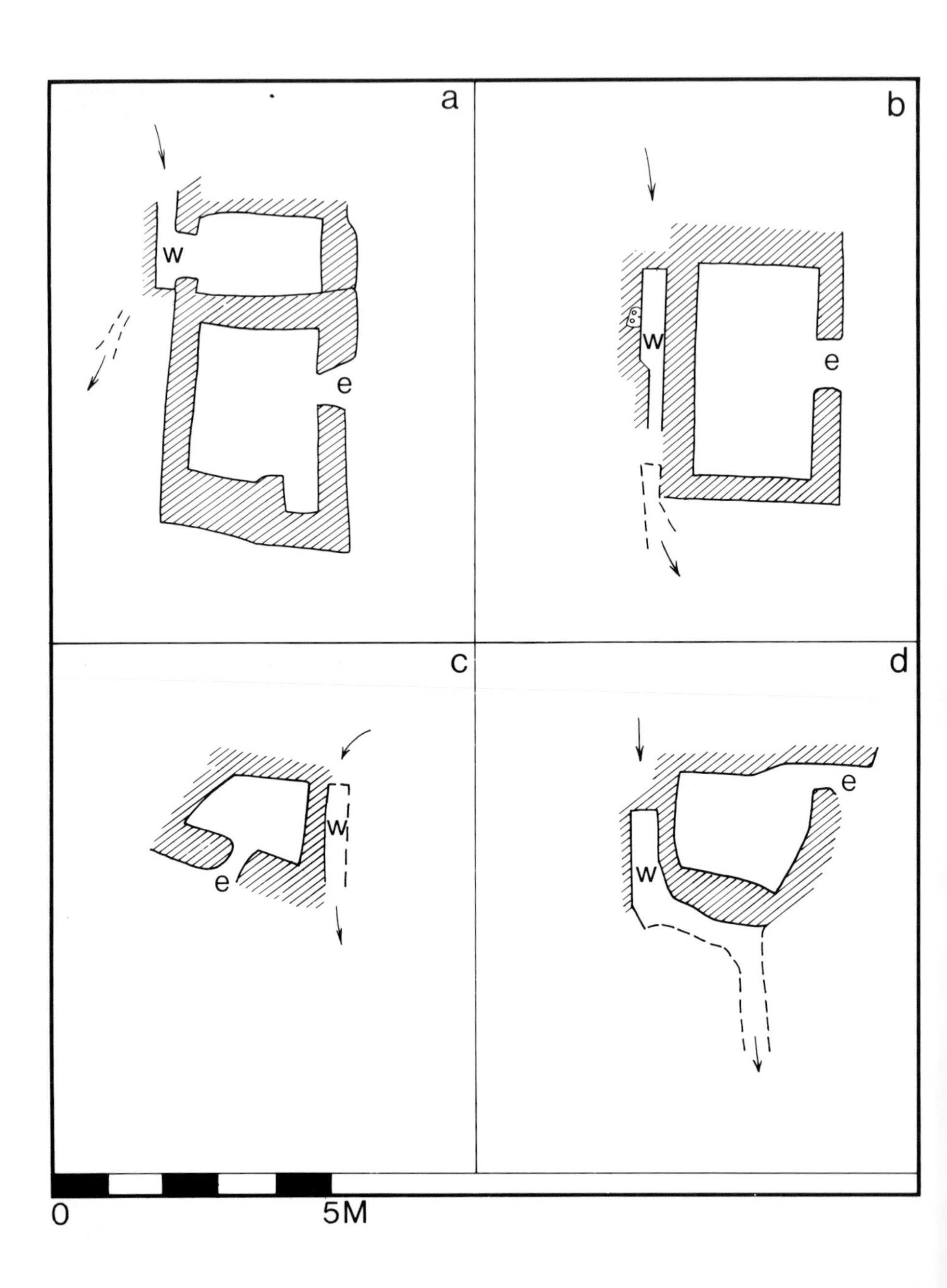
a
w
e
b
w
e
c
w
e
d
e
w
0
5M

the standard means of achieving this. This was not just the case for the south-west tin industry but also for use with many types of ore in many regions of the world. Georgius Agricola, the 16th-century German author of a major treatise on mining and ore processing techniques, illustrates and describes stamping mills used for tin and other metals in 1556 (Fig. 17) when the technique had clearly long been practiced in Europe.[14] In south-west Britain, early documentation suggests that stamping mills were in use by 1400 in Cornwall[15] and 1504 in Devon[16], though in both cases undocumented mills would certainly have been at work even earlier.

The principle behind the stamping mill is that vertically set reciprocating balks of timber, with iron shod lower ends, were dropped on to the tin ore after being raised to a certain height by power from the waterwheel. The reciprocal action was achieved by placing pegs or tappets in the rear of the stamps timbers which engaged on corresponding cams, or lifters, protruding from a drive shaft, powered directly from the waterwheel(Fig 15). As the shaft rotated the cams would raise the stamps, usually arranged in a set of two or three in a row, then release them to fall onto the ore, which was shovelled in by hand, crushing it against a hard surface.

A later innovation to the stamping mill was the addition of a flow of water around the stamp heads, contained within a stout wooden box known as the stamps box, which was partially sunk into the ground. This would enable the crushed ore to be washed through a finely perforated grate at the front of the stamps box, after sufficient stamping, allowing the operation to be one of continuous feed rather than in the earlier dry stamping mill where it is likely that the mill had to be stopped to remove the crushed tinstone from the stamps. This transition probably occurred in the early 16th century in Europe when Agricola wrote of its inventor, one Sigismund Maltitz: '*he invented a machine which could crush the ore wet under iron-shod stamps*'.[17] Richard Carew, writing only a few years later, said of Cornish practice: '*howbeit of late times they mostly use wet stampers and so have no need of Crazing Mills for their best stuff*'.[18] We may assume therefore that wet stamping had become a standard practice by the second half of the 16th century in the west of England too. This statement also unwittingly tells us of the demise of the crazing mill.

The most important field remains to be found at the site of a stamping mill is the mortarstone. These are the hard surfaces onto which the stamps struck the ore and consist of flat-faced granite boulders of up to 1 m long, with cup-shaped

Fig. 13. Simplified ground plans of stamping-mills. a) Black Tor Falls left bank (SX 5748 7163); b) Colesmill (SX 5935 6676); c) Plym (SX 6746 6742); d) Outcombe (SX 5801 6860).
Key: e = entrance; w = wheelpit. Arrow indicates flow of water from leat.

Plate 9 (above left). Double mortarstone at Black Tor Falls SX 5749 7161. Scale = 30cm.
Plate 10 (above right). Mortarstone with four hollows (i.e. two sets of two) at Runnage SX 6716 7957. Scale = 1m.
Plate 11 (left) Triple mortarstone at Venford SX 6856 7118. Scale = 30cm

hollows, arranged in twos, threes, or fours on one or more face. The hollows, which are sometimes circular but more often elliptical, are on average 16.5cm by 18.5cm on the short and long axis respectively, though extremes may be 11cm and 35cm. The depth may be up to 9.5cm deep[19]. They are most commonly arranged in pairs, demonstrating the use of two heads of stamps, although several triple mortarstones have also been recorded at Week Ford, Venford (Plate 11) and Nosworthy right bank where three stamps were clearly in use. R.H. Worth established that the between-centres measurement of the hollows on a mortarstone could vary between 23cm and 35cm.[20]

Where four hollows exist on one face, this does not indicate four stamps in use but two pairs of two, where the stone has been realigned under the stamps at some point in its career to offer fresh stamping surfaces. This became necessary as the hollows wore too deep to be effective and had to be replaced. A very fine stone with four hollows on two faces has been built into an enclosure wall beside the Wallabrook near Runnage (Plate 10). Excessive wearing of hollows would also explain the existence of mortarstones with

Plate 12 (left). Upper crazing mill stone at Gobbet tin mill (SX 6453 7280).

Plate 13 (right). Lower crazing mill stone at Gobbet tin mill. Scale = 1m

hollows on two or more faces, as well as the many apparently discarded mortars at some mill sites.

At Upper Merrivale the excavations have revealed that some disused mortarstones were, at a later date, used as building material when the mill was rebuilt, probably as a blowing mill. With this in mind we can now no longer be sure that sites containing evidence for both blowing and stamping had had both operations occurring simultaneously, and the remains could represent two phases of different activity in the same building.

Crazing mills are far less numerous with only three examples having so-far been recorded at Sheepstor, Outcombe and Gobbet. Unfortunately the example from Outcombe, recorded and photographed by R.H. Worth in the 1930s has since been removed and its current whereabouts are unknown.[21] At Gobbet both the upper and lower stones survive at the site. The lower, fixed stone, has a diameter of 1.2m and a smooth top surface while the upper stone, which rotated is smaller at only 90cm. It also is smooth on one side with a domed top. Both stones have a hole in their centres and the upper stone also has four smaller holes, positioned diametrically in pairs on the top to accommodate cranks from the waterwheel. There is no certainty as to how exactly this worked, although in Worth's photograph of the missing Outcombe upper stone, a dovetailed recess in the bottom of the stone to house a tongue from the shaft, resembles a system described and depicted by Agricola.[22] Tinstone would have been fed in through the hole in the top stone, to be collected around the edges

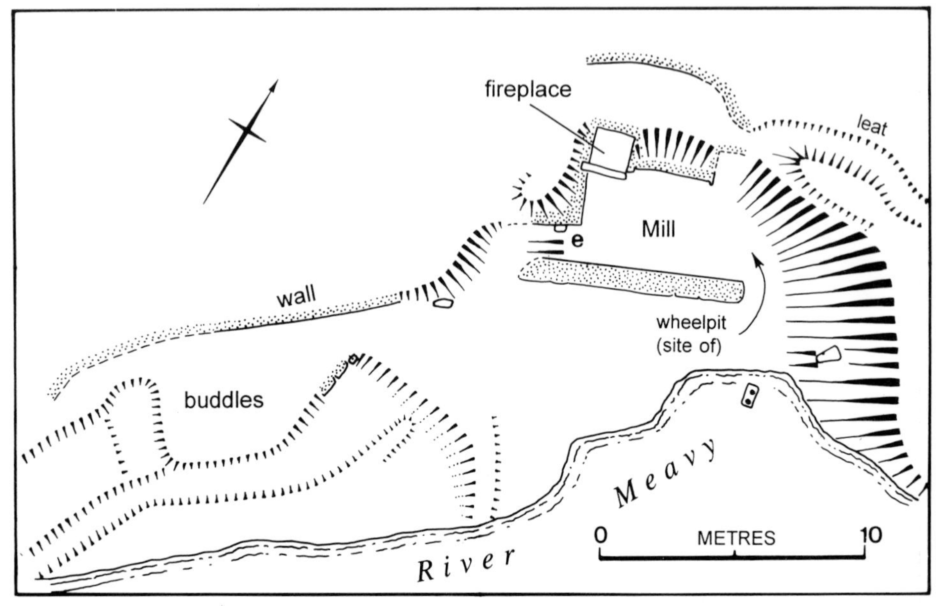

Fig.14. Simplified earthwork plan of Black Tor Falls right bank tin mill (SX 5748 7166). The mill is well-preserved though the extent of the wheelpit is obscured by fallen masonry. The clear evidence of a dressing floor with a rear retaining wall and at least one buddle is the best of its type so-far discovered at an early tin mill on Dartmoor.

after crushing. It would need to be reasonably fine before being fed into the mill so it is likely that crazing mills were mostly used for the purer alluvial gravels, before the coarser lode ores were being exploited, or perhaps to augment the less-efficient, early dry stamp mills. Carew's testimony for the demise of the crazing mill as the technology moved on, quoted above, is nicely complemented by the evidence of the lower stone at Gobbet which has two mortarstone hollows on its flat surface, indicating that although the crazing mill had become redundant, this large, flat stone itself was still usable as the base for its replacement, the stamping mill.

DRESSING FLOORS

When crushed to a suitably fine state the cassiterite had to be separated from the unwanted sands(gangue), an operation known as 'dressing'. The technique of tin dressing has always relied on the fact that particles of cassiterite are far

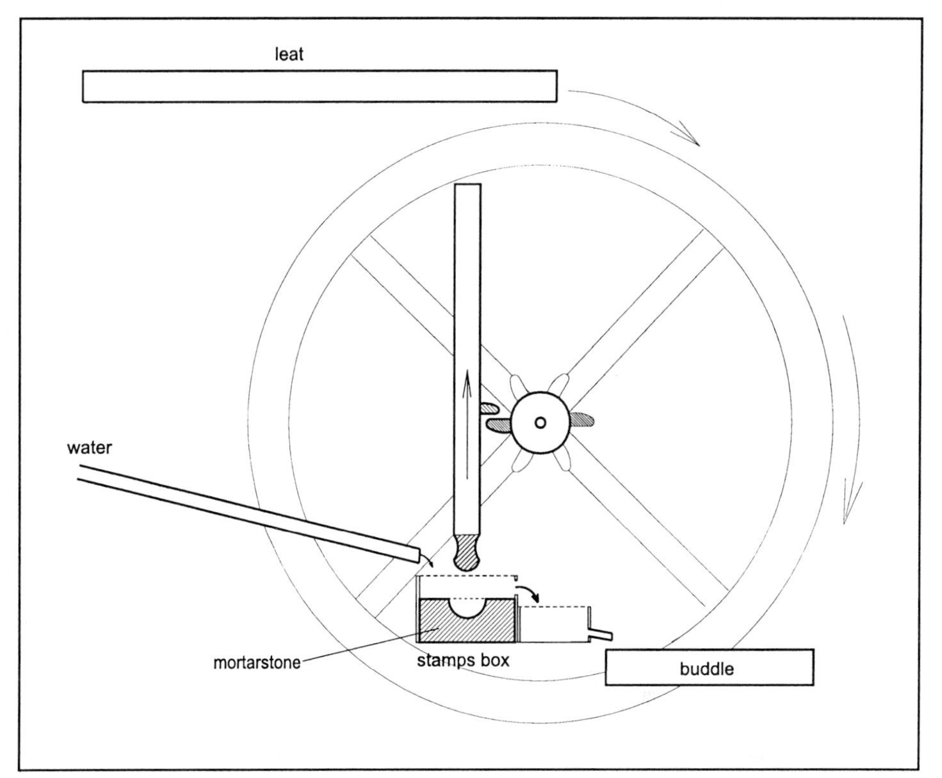

Fig. 15. Elevation of the machinery contained within a tin stamping mill.

heavier than particles of the unwanted minerals or gangue of equal size. Consequently, when combined with moving water the tin sinks faster than the gangue, which can be carried away by the continued movement of the water, thus separating the two elements.

In the first stamping mills, where tin was stamped dry, we cannot be sure exactly how this process was put into effect but it is likely that dressing took place in large wooden tubs, or within portable troughs, neither of which are likely to have left us with much archaeological evidence. With the advent of wet stamping however, we have some contemporary accounts of how the process of dressing was carried out. After passing through the grate of the stamping mill the water and crushed tinstone, ran via a channel into long, rectangular pits or wooden troughs known as buddles, where the heavier tin would accumulate at the head, while the gangue was kept moving by the flow of the water. After separation, the tin was then shovelled out and the settling process was repeated

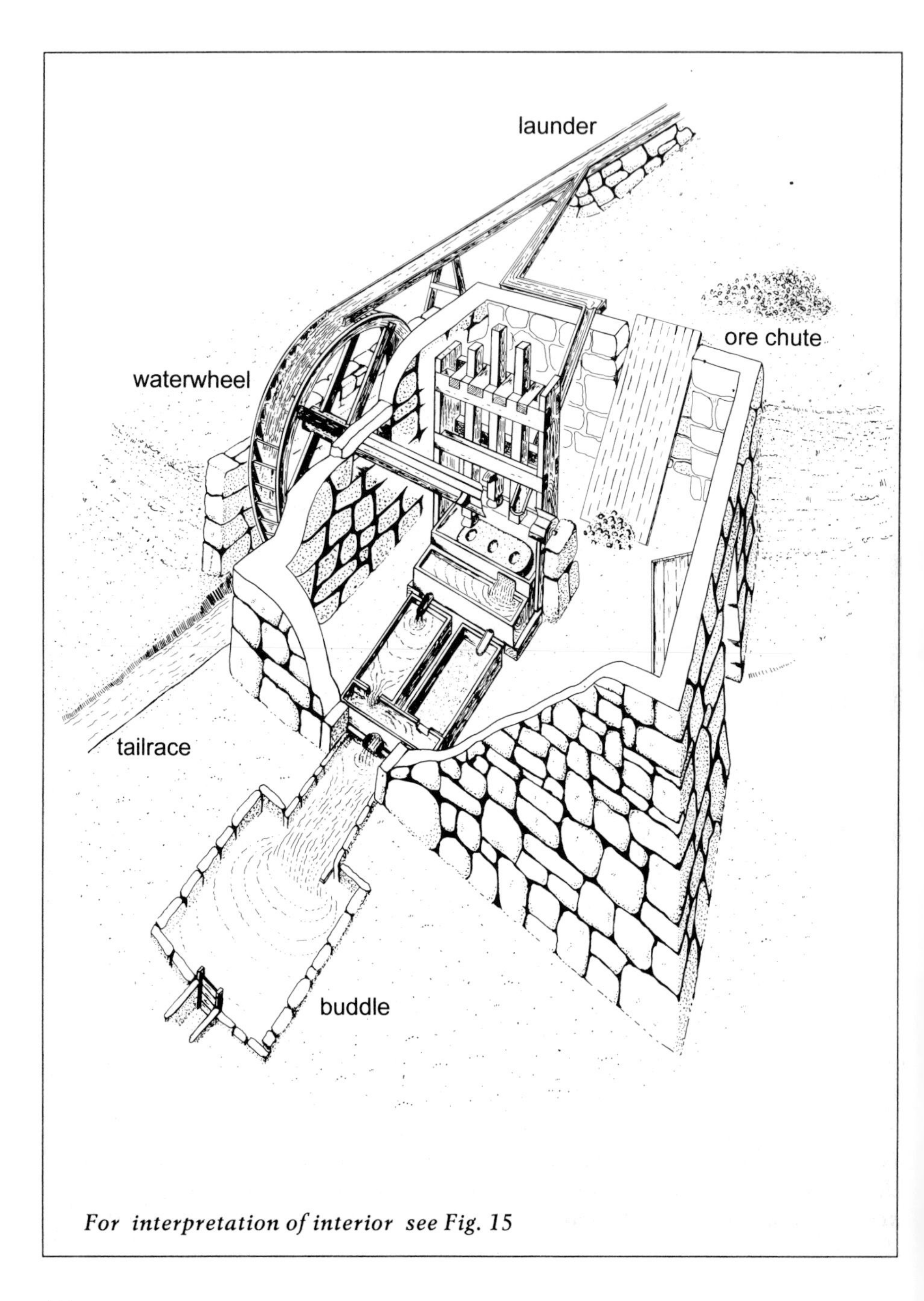

For interpretation of interior see Fig. 15

Fig. 17(above). Woodcut of a 16th-century, European tin mill from Agricola's De Re Metallica *of 1556.*

Fig. 16(left). Reconstruction of an early tin stamping mill, based very loosely on the structure at Colesmill *(Fig. 13b). The illustration is of a wet stamping mill with three heads of stamps, internal and external buddles. It is possible the ore chute may have led directly into the stamps box at more developed mills. The stamps frame, wooden buddles and water feed to the stamps box are all based on the tin stamping mill engraving in Agricola(1556).*

in further buddles. Agricola's 1556 illustration of a wet stamping mill (Fig. 17) shows all of these details[23] and an anonymous English writer of 1671, describes a similar system, mentioning an elongated trench '.. *stopped at the other end with turf, so that the water runs away and the ore sinks to the bottom: which when full is taken up (ie emptied) with shovel'*.[24]

Field evidence for these early buddles has only recently begun to be recognised and in any case usually consists of very subtle earthworks, barely perceivable to the casual eye. However, several examples are known including those at Upper Merrivale which have now been archaeologically excavated. At Gobbet there is some evidence of buddles to the east of the mill but one of the clearest examples is to be seen at Black Tor Falls right bank (Fig.14). Here a revetment wall has been built to the west of the mill creating a level terrace beside the river. Placed obliquely within the level area, is a shallow, rectangular pit, with some evidence of a stone lining along one side. A channel, now visible by the lush growth of reeds taking advantage of its silty state, led water used in the buddle out and back into the river below.

At many sites where tin was crushed and dressed, the waste material, usually referred to as tin slimes, may be observed. It is a very fine silty sand, usually silver or white in colour, and can often be found stratified into eroded sections of river banks, downstream of the mill.

Although we now have a substantial body of information about tin mills, both archaeological and through contemporary accounts of their use, attempting to reconstruct their appearance and fully understand how the processes were carried out within them is hampered to some extent by the knowledge we still do not possess. Archaeological excavation has supplied a little more data, but this form of investigation is still relatively new at tin milling sites. In any case many important components of the mills certainly do not survive as archaeological evidence so several parts of the puzzle are still missing. Bearing these limitations in mind, Figs 11 and 16 are attempts at explaining how stamping and blowing mills may have appeared, and how their machinery may have functioned. Neither is an accurate reconstruction of a genuine site though both are based on the interior layout of existing mills.

Grid references for examples in chapter 3

Avon Dam	SX 6722 6553 (visible only at times of drought)
Blacksmith's Shop	SX 6377 8426
Black Tor Falls	SX 574- 716-
Broad Falls	SX 6543 6692
Colesmill	SX 5935 6676
Gobbett	SX 6453 7280
Longstone Sheepstor	SX 5560 6842 (no public access)
Lower Merrivale	SX 5526 7535
Middle Merrivale	SX 5527 7624
Nosworthy Left Bank	SX 5678 6958
Outcombe	SX 5801 6860
Plym (small)	SX 6746 6742
Runnage	SX 6716 7957
Taw	SX 6205 9197
Upper Merrivale	SX 5519 7664
Venford	SX 6856 7118
Week Ford	SX 6618 7232 (no public access)

References

1. Gerrard 1989, 12
2. Worth 1953, 310-11
3. Worth 1953, 289
4. Gerrard 1989, 9
5. DRO 48/14/40/3
6. Greeves 1992, 47
7. Gerrard & Greeves 1992,4
8. Worth 1953, 287
9. Worth 1953, 316
10. Beare 1586, 108
11. Pryce 1778, 136
12. Beare 1586, 106
13. ibid, 107
14. Agricola 1556
15. Gerrard 1989, 10
16. Amery 1924, 51
17. Agricola 1556, 312
18. Carew 1602, 39
19. based on figures from Greeves 1981, 204
20. Worth 1953, 326
21. ibid, 320
22. Agricola 1556, 294
23. ibid, 314
24. Anon 1670, 2108(Quoted in Austin *et al* 1989, 101)

4

Tinners' Huts

The term Tinners' Hut has been applied to a variety of structures on Dartmoor, usually because of their close or direct association with tinworks.

A glance at the larger scale Ordnance Survey maps of Dartmoor will reveal the existence of a good number of Tinners' Huts, though there are indeed many more not marked on the map. During a recent survey of Dartmoor Forest, for example, which contains a good proportion of the central Dartmoor uplands, a total of 94 of these buildings were recorded.[1]

However, the term Tinners' Hut, which by implication suggests that these structures were constructed and used exclusively by tinners, sometimes needs to be questioned as there is no real evidence, historical or otherwise besides their location, to prove this to be so. Similar structures when sited away from tinworks are traditionally assigned the title of Peat Cutters' or Shepherds' shelters. There is therefore the possibility that users of the high moors, other than tinners, constructed their shelters in old tinworkings to take advantage of the suitability of the sites, with their easily adapted location, ready supply of loose stone and a certain amount of protection from the weather, often in areas where no natural shelter exists. Nevertheless, even with this in mind it seems likely that many of these huts, were indeed built and used as places of shelter by the tinners.

These small, roofless, rectangular ruins are mostly sited within areas of streamworking, where their builders often took advantage of existing man-made features, such as mounds of discarded stone, into which the huts are built. Where such mounds are systematically constructed and evenly spaced, this creates ideal situations for the siting of a building. Such is the case for one example at Brim Brook, where a hut has been positioned between two parallel waste heaps. Where the working is less systematic they will occupy low hollows or are built against the outer scarp of the working. An example of this may be seen on the south bank of the O Brook, where a fine hut is built into the scarp at the bend in the river. Utilising such existing features would give walls extra thickness, give some shelter from the elements and minimise building effort. The walls are usually constructed from roughly coursed, unhewn granite and where built into a mound, consist simply of a vertical

Plate 14. A well-preserved Tinners' Hut near Hookney Tor SX 6953 8123.

revetment. Huts are also to be found sited within openworks where the artificially lowered position gave effective shelter from the extremes of Dartmoor weather. At Wheal Prosper two such examples may be seen.

The size of the structures varies between approximately 2m and 6m in length and up to 4m wide. The constructed walls, (in contrast to those which utilise existing features) can be up to 2m thick, although 0.8m is more typical. The walls are usually ruinous and seldom remain to a height in excess of 1m, except in exceptional cases; most are lower with tumbled stone from the walls covering the interior. Entrances survive on many huts, consisting usually only of a break in one of the walls. Stone door jambs are uncommon though may be observed at one or two sites. On the whole however it would appear that doors would have been fairly basic, without hinges or fixtures, or that the jambs as well as the doors, were constructed from timber and have not survived. Fireplace openings are visible in some of the better preserved tinners huts, although they - or their survival - are also uncommon. These consist of a recess, 0.5 - 0.8m wide, built into the interior extending for the full height. Chimneys have survived at very few sites, the hut at Beckamoor Combe probably housing the best example, though this is only as high as the wall itself.

Plate 15 . The Tinners' Cache or beehive hut known as Downing's House on the River Erme SX 6395 6293.

It is not possible to assign dates to individual Tinners' Huts without archaeological excavation, though even this might be inconclusive, but it seems likely that shelters would have been necessary over the entire period that tin was being exploited on Dartmoor. The need for them may indeed have been more acute during the earlier period when Dartmoor's upland was more remote and travel between the border settlements and high moors would have been difficult. On-site accommodation was probably essential, though examples from this date would be the least easily recognised.

Good examples of Tinners' Huts may be seen at locations all over the high moors, within valleys which have been worked for tin. The Brim Brook valley contains four huts, each of differing characteristics, including one likely to be of 19th-century date associated with a small documented mine called Wheal Providence.[2] Other areas worth exploring for Tinners' Huts are Blacklane Brook, Hortonsford Bottom and Newleycombe Lake. All the tributaries of the River Swincombe are furnished with Tinners' Huts and the River Avon has fine examples at Avon Head and at Fish Lake.

TINNERS' CACHES

The idea of the cache where tinners would hide tools and ingots or house illicit stils for the making of liquor is well rooted in Dartmoor lore and probably has some basis in fact though it is unlikely that there were quite as many as some recent writers have assumed. Many of the recorded caches consist of naturally placed rocks, which have been undermined during streaming creating small chambers which certainly could have made convenient stores, shelters or places of concealment if needed: there is one good example in the Newleycombe Valley. Other caches may have been constructed by placing large slabs over a hollow or other upright stones to form an artificial chamber such as that at Stonetor Bottom. Some caches however were very much grander such as that at Downing's House beside the River Erme. This is a well constructed chamber with roof still in place and sufficient space inside to shelter a person if necessary.

Grid references for examples in chapter 4

Avon Head	SX 6497 6965
Beckamoor Combe	SX 5351 7570
Blacklane Brook	SX 6295 6769
Brim Brook	SX 5890 8753
Downing's House	SX 6395 6293
Fish Lake	SX 6461 6806
Hortonsford Bottom	SX 6236 6591
Newleycombe Cache	SX 5930 7000
Newleycombe Lake	SX 5950 7095
O Brook	SX 6508 7130
Stonetor Bottom	SX 648 858
Wheal Prosper	SX 5725 7936
Wheal Providence	SX 5887 8732

References

1. Newman 1996, 143-9
2. Le Messurier 1979, 59-73

5

The Later Period

During the early 18th century the Dartmoor tin industry declined in its importance quite dramatically. This is reflected in the tin production figures which, after a brief 'blip' in 1706, had fallen to nothing by 1750.[1] Many reasons could be attributed to this decline, such as falling demand, but more than anything it is likely to be due to the near total exhaustion of Dartmoor's easily exploitable tin sources. Rich alluvial deposits were all but gone and shallower lodes had probably been worked to the limit of existing technology; only deeper tin lodes remained to be tapped profitably. Although some very small operations may have continued through the mid-18th century, producing insignificant quantities of tin, it was not until the later part of that century that a revival in the fortunes of the industry came about as the Industrial Revolution brought with it the dual benefits of a fresh demand for all metals, and improved mining technology. The spirit of the age was also very much one of optimism, reflected in other ways on Dartmoor such as the renewed efforts to cultivate large tracts of the upland using 'modern' farming techniques. Nevertheless, both mining and agriculture on Dartmoor proved financially risky and often disastrous for those who took part.

Historically the late 18th and the 19th-century tin industry on Dartmoor is characterised by small companies of mining venturers, who, with the help of outside investors, would embark on small and often rather dubious mining enterprises. Despite the mines sometimes possessing optimistic sounding names, like Wheal Fortune, Wheal Lucky and Wheal Prosper, they seldom lived up to expectation, and individual companies did not usually stay afloat for very long. The documented history of several of Dartmoor's tin mines has been well disscussed elsewhere and they include Wheal Cumpston[2], Steeperton Tor Mine[3] and Eylesbarrow Mine [4]. Some of the smaller mines would pass from one company to the next, producing insignificant quantities of tin if any. Larger mines with good levels of productivity did exist though, despite the vicissitudes of insolvent companies. Eylesbarrow Mine was producing tin for the entire first half of the 19th century, in respectable quantities, as was the Vitifer and Birch Tor area which sustained several mining enterprises between the 1780s and the early 1930s, mining lodes which had been worked probably for two or three centuries before.[5]

UNDERGROUND WORKING

Nearly all these mines, with only one or two exceptions, re-worked lodes which had been exploited previously by earlier techniques, utilising the ability to penetrate the lodes to greater depths than before by going underground. Underground mining technology had long been available to the tinners, with pumping equipment in use in metal mines as early as the 15th century.[6] We cannot be at all sure of a date for its first use as a viable technique for Dartmoor tin, but the added problems of extremely wet conditions on the moors had perhaps always excluded miners going to greater depths until more advanced pumping equipment was introduced, particularly if more accessible sources of tin were still available in streamworks and shallow lode works. The availability of more effective explosives must also have eased the problems of working hard rock underground.

To work a lode from underground it was necessary to dig or 'drive' horizontal tunnels called adits or levels, into the hillside connected to vertical shafts which

Plate 16. Surface evidence of 19th-century shafts at Wheal Caroline (SX 6682 8122), with the characteristic half-moon shape ring of spoil around the circumference.

ventilated the mine. The lode could then be worked or 'stoped' either from above or below depending on where the level made contact with the vein. The lowest adit which could be open to the air was the drainage level and any levels lower than this would need to be pumped to prevent flooding.

Most of the adits on Dartmoor have since become blocked either by collapse or growth of vegetation or a combination of both. Even when completely blocked they may still often be recognised in the field today by the finger or half-moon shaped spoil heaps of stone and soil which extend from the opening. Good examples of the latter are to be seen at Steeperton Tor Mine. The openings themselves will sometimes have water issuing from within and, along with the drainage channels which lead away down the hillside, will support sphagnum moss, rushes and other moisture loving species. Several adit openings have survived such as at Keaglesborough Mine, Eylesbarrow Mine (Two Brothers Adit) and Bush Down, all of which may still be entered for a few metres, though it would be unwise to do so.

Shafts which in nearly all cases have been capped for safety reasons since becoming disused, remain only as surface evidence. Where shafts were sunk on previously undisturbed ground, they survive as conical pits, with crescentic rings of spoil on the downslope side which can usually be distinguished from their earlier counterpart, the lodeback pits, by their larger size and sharper, fresher looking earthworks. There is also usually a lot less of them. Fine examples are to be seen at Wheal Caroline(Plate 16) to the north-west of the Warren House Inn, and at Whiteworks where in several cases they have been walled off. Shafts were very often dug into the trenches of earlier openworks and survive as conical indentations in the base of the working. Several quite large examples of this may be seen at Vitifer but also at Gobbet.

The pump would be powered by a waterwheel which if possible would be sited near the head of a shaft, down which a system of vertically reciprocating push rods would operate the pumps. Remains of such a setup may be seen at a small mine called Plym Consols, in the Newleycombe Valley where the stone-lined wheelpit sits only a few metres from the shafthead. Built into a hollow adjacent to the shaft is another three sided-structure which housed a device called a balance bob. This was a pivoted counter-weight which converted the horizontal movement of the push-rods into the vertical movement needed to

Plate 17 (top). Wheelpit and dressing floors at Eylesbarrow Mine in the Plym Valley (SX 5939 6777). See also Fig. 18.

Plate 18 (lower). A rectangular buddle at Eylesbarrow Mine. Note the stone lined sides and central water outlet on the narrow end.

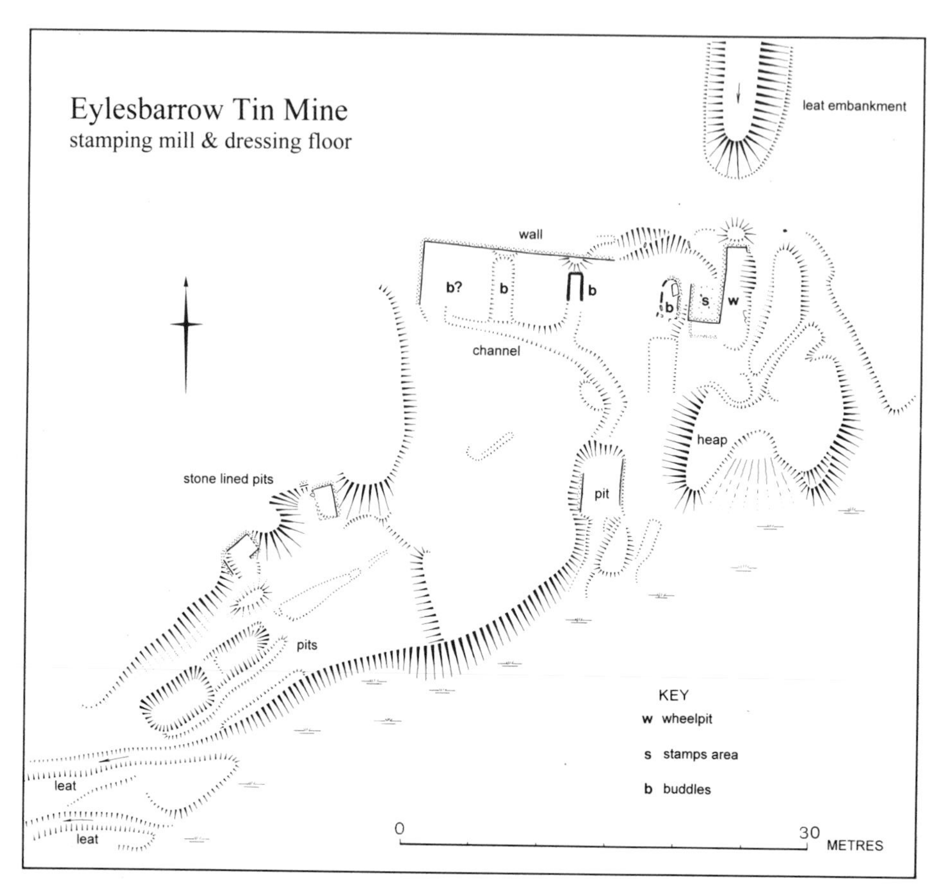

Fig. 18. Earthwork plan of one of the dressing floors at Eylesbarrow Mine (SX 5939 6777), showing the wheelpit at the eastern end of the floor and the arrangement of various rectangular buddles and settling pits (See Pl. 17).

power the pumps down on the lower levels. Several large wheelpits which housed pumping wheels, and their accompanying bob pits may be seen at Vitifer and at Golden Dagger Mine where the shaft which housed the pumping equipment sits within the old openwork and the pumping wheel is sited adjacent a few metres away. At some mines, where shaftheads were sited quite high on the hillside, sufficient water supplies to power the large wheels necessary to do this job were not available and waterwheels needed to be positioned lower down the hill away from the shaft. In these cases a horizontal system of flat rods, supported on upright posts, would transmit the power, often over great distances from the wheel to the balance bob. At Eylesbarrow, the later pumping wheel had a diameter of approximately 50ft(c15.4m)[7] - the largest on Dartmoor - and a series of paired, granite posts, each with semicircular grooves to house pulley axles, on the top surface, may be seen running up the hillside to the bob pits sited at the heads of the shafts. Hexworthy mine also had flat rod systems and until quite recently several of the pulley wheels were still visible, on the ground. One of these may be seen in the Museum of Dartmoor Life at Okehampton. A particularly fine pumping wheelpit survives at Huntingdon Mine on the Western Wella Brook.

Steam power was used rarely at Dartmoor tin mines, where close proximity of reliable water supplies enabled water wheels to be used for most operations where power was required. Nevertheless, at Ringleshuttes, a remote mine in the Holne district, which was sited well above any reliable source of water, there are the remains of a rectangular structure beside a shafthead, which undoubtedly once housed steam-powered pumping or winding equipment. The circular base of the chimney is still visible and a linear spread of rubble to the east represents the collapsed stack. It is likely to have closely resembled the engine house at Wheal Betsy copper mine near Peter Tavy, which is Dartmoor's most notable surviving example, though would have been on a smaller scale.

DRESSING FLOORS

Smelting of tin rarely took place at all on the high moors after the early 18th century and only one smelting site which was operating into the 19th century has left any significant remains, at Eylesbarrow, though this was disused by 1831[8]. However, with the lower grades of ore extracted from mines, an efficient dressing process was more necessary than ever to separate the cassiterite from the impurities of the country rock, and the processing areas known as dressing floors became highly developed to do this, although the essential principles of tin dressing varied little from those used at the 16th and 17th-century stamping mills.

The field remains for these later processing sites usually conform to a fairly standard layout and consist of a level terrace with a reveted stone retaining wall to the rear. A wheelpit will sit either to one end of the wall, or sometimes centrally, and would have contained an overshot, or pitchback waterwheel. Behind the wheelpit there is usually a substantial leat embankment, necessary to give sufficient height for the water on these much larger waterwheels, which could be up to 8m diameter. The wheel would have powered a set of stamps, similar to those in the earlier tin mills but more numerous and on a larger scale, using the same principle of a rotating shaft with protruding tappets engaging

onto corresponding cams on the upright stamps. These later mills did not use mortarstones as a crushing surface, but thick rammed quartz contained within a masonry or iron surround[9].

Positioned on the level area of the dressing floor will be a range of shallow rectangular pits, often lined with masonry. These are the buddles and, unlike their counterparts found at earlier tin mills, they often remain in good condition. Good examples may be seen at Keaglesborough Mine, near Burrator and at Eylesbarrow Mine, where several dressing floors survive in a good state(Plate 18; Fig. 18). Examples of smaller dressing floors survive at Wheal Fortune and East Hughes Mine. At larger sites there would often be two or more dressing floors, arranged on the slope in such a way as to take advantage of a single water supply. The most developed example of this is at Eylesbarrow where six floors are aligned along the Drizzlecombe Valley.

A later innovation for the buddle was its circular form. The principle of gravity separation in moving water was still the essence of the operation but in the circular buddle the crushed tin and water, known as 'pulp', was introduced onto a central cone and settled outwards over a conical, inclined surface. The purer tin, being heavier, would accumulate nearer the centre or 'head', while the less pure material (middle head) settled further from the centre and the waste or 'tailings' would come to rest around the peripheries. The deposit would build up to between 6 and 12 inches (15 - 30cm). The three grades of concentrate could then be easily separated with the tailings being discarded and the middle head being passed to another buddle of slightly different specification. Small waterwheels sited near the buddles were used to power rotating arms or sweeps which passed just above the surface of the buddle floor and from which pieces of fabric dangled into the water to give the sediments the appropriate movement. There are many well-preserved circular buddles surviving on Dartmoor, though the inclined surfaces and any other timber components are no longer visible. Two particularly large examples may be seen at Wheal Frederick but others survive at West Vitifer Mine and at Golden Dagger(Plate 19). At Hexworthy Mine two buddles with concrete outer kerbs, dating from the 20th century are visible at the main dressing floor, the whole of which was once covered by large sheds. At the latter site and some other 20th-century mines, concrete was used

Plate 19 (top). A well-preserved circular buddle of the 20th century at Golden Dagger Mine (SX 6845 8000).

Plate 20 (lower). The remains of a Granite mine building at Wheal Frederick (SX 545 78540). Few buildings at Dartmoor tin mines are in this good a state of preservation, many having been demolished for misguided conservation and safety reasons.

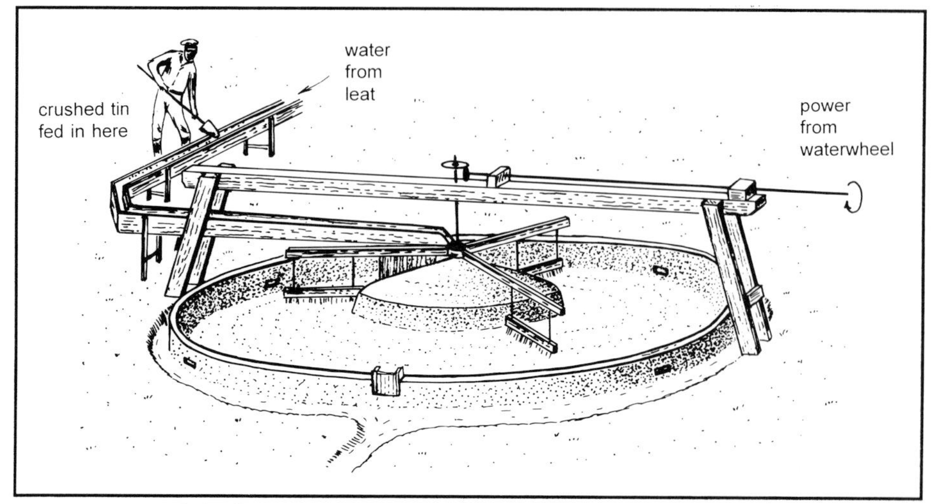

Fig. 19. Simplified reconstruction of 19th - 20th-century circular buddle. There were many variations on the circular buddle system, which were used at both tin and lead mines, including concave and convex, each for refining separate grades of concentrate. The most common at Dartmoor tin mines was the convex form with a central cone and sloping floor as in the illustration. Some were constructed from concrete, others from stone or brick while others were of timber. This drawing is loosely based on the buddles photographed at Golden Dagger Mine while still operating in the 1920s (Greeves 1986, 60-62). The power to drive the sweeps came from a rotating axle running along the top of the buddle frame, driven by a small waterwheel. The buddles were often arranged in rows of two or three so the same wheel and axle could drive several buddles.

extensively in the construction of dressing floors and buddles, and temporary, corrugated iron structures were placed over them for shelter. Also unusual at Hexworthy was the fact that the processing equipment within the sheds, together with the winding equipment at the nearby shaft, were powered by electricity, generated by a water turbine adjacent to the O Brook at Saddle Bridge, 1.5km from the dressing floor.

Dressing floors would produce copious quantities of a fine, silvery waste sand known as tin slimes and the final resting place for this after passing through all the refining processes would be a tailings pond into which the waste was transported in moving water via wooden water channels. Though disguised by vegetation at some sites, this material is visible at the Hexworthy Mine upper

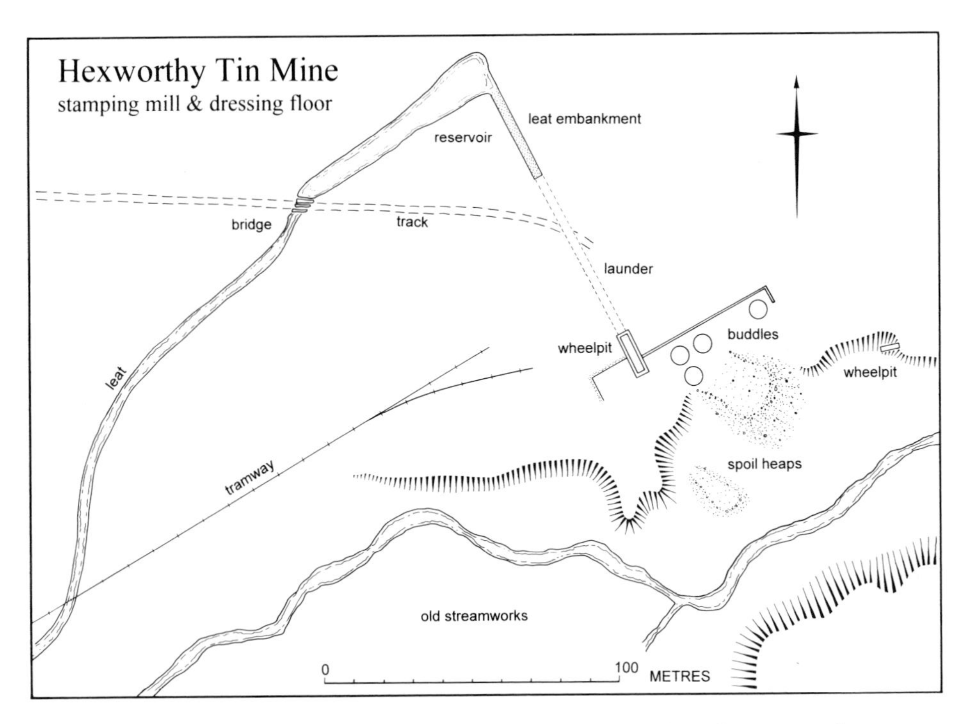

Fig. 20. Plan with interpretation of the Dry Lake dressing floors at Hexworthy Mine (SX 6605 7110), showing circular buddles, wheelpits, reservoir and tramway. The interpretation shows elements of the site in use in about 1900, before the wheel was adapted for pumping (after* RCHME *1996, ©Crown Copyright).

floors below and to the east of which is a massive flat-topped mound, scarred by rabbit holes revealing the tin slimes.

There were many additional processes beyond stamping and buddling necessary to dress tin, which because they left little or no field evidence are beyond the scope of this book. However, unlike the earlier periods of the tin industry, where the documentary record is scanty and many operations and practices we may understand very imprecisely, for the 19th and 20th century we have photographic and documentary evidence, and, most important, the personal recollections of those who worked at tin mines. These aspects of the later Dartmoor tin industry are covered by existing publications (see Greeves, 1986; Richardson 1992).

OTHER ABOVE GROUND REMAINS

Often associated with the mines is a range of ancillary buildings and structures, which housed workshops, accommodation, machinery, drying areas and offices. These remain usually only as crumbling ruins today though in one or two cases, the walls stand to a good height, such as at Wheal Frederick on Doe Tor Brook (Fig. 20) where the four granite walls of a substantial single storey structure survive almost intact. Sadly this site is exceptional as many such buildings became the victims of demolition in the pre-conservation days of the 20th century.

Perhaps the best range of buildings is to be seen at Vitifer and Golden Dagger, two mines set close together in the Redwater Valley and both working earlier this century. Many ruined structures may be seen scattered along the track some of which were marked on larger scale Ordnance Survey maps. The buildings today are mostly ruined to foundation level, having suffered a program of demolition after the Second World War, although several have survived slightly better, such as the building known as Dinah's House, which was occupied by mining families up until the 1930s.

Tramways were often used for transporting the raw mined tinstone to the dressing floors, which could be positioned some distance from the adit. Simple side tipping skips, set on four wheels could be drawn along the iron rails either by horse power or by water power. The rails do not usually survive but the flat-topped trackways on which they were set are to be seen at some sites. Evidence of several sections of tramway exists at Vitifer and at Wheal Frederick a very clear example survives. At Ringleshuttes a long straight trackway leading from the mine down to a probable dressing area near Venford Brook is particularly clear and at Hexworthy Mine, subtle earthwork remains mark the position where timber sleepers once lay and the course of the tramway between the two sections of the site is visible.

The later period of tin mining on Dartmoor from the 18th to early 20th century, is in terms of tin production a very insignificant episode for the industry as a whole, covering a relatively short period of a long history, but in terms of field remains it greatly enhances the types of evidence to be seen on Dartmoor today. Exploration of these sites can be particularly rewarding with many of the key elements often surviving to be witnessed by the observant. Unlike the earlier period of tin working in the South-West however - where, because of the unique characteristics of alluvial tin, the extraction and processing evidence is very specialised - the later mining methods used for lode tin would have been familiar to miners searching for other metals. Dartmoor's border areas have a good share of these and evidence of a very similar nature is to be found at copper, iron and lead/silver mines within Dartmoor National Park.

Grid references for examples in chapter 5

Brimpts Mine	SX 6655 7385 (centred)
Bush Down	SX 6800 8180
Dinah's House	SX 6846 8002
East Hughes Mine	SX 5925 6995
Eylesbarrow Tin Mine	SX 5980 6910 (centred)
Gobbett Mine	SX 6465 7282
Golden Dagger	SX 6830 8020 (centred)
Hexworthy Mine	SX 6605 7110 (lower dressing floor)
Hexworthy Mine	SX 6566 7082 (upper dressing floor)
Hexworthy Mine	SX 6644 7190 (turbine house)
Huntingdon Mine	SX 6658 6650 (pumping wheelpit)
Keaglesborough	SX 5737 7012
Plym Consols	SX 5860 6988
Ringleshuttes	SX 6753 6987 (engine house)
SteepertonTor Mine	SX 6140 8840
Vitifer & Birch Tor	SX 680- 810- (centred)
Wheal Betsy	SX 5102 8138
Wheal Caroline	SX 668- 812-
Wheal Cumpston	SX 6717 7235
Wheal Fortune	SX 5493 7540
Wheal Frederick	SX 5457 8540
Whiteworks	SX 613- 710- (centred)

References

1. Worth 1953, 287.
2. Greeves 1978, 161-71.
3. Greeves 1985, 101-127.
4. Cook et al 1974, 161-214.
5. Broughton 1968-9.
6. Claughton 1996.
7. Cook et al 1974, 180.
8. ibid, 167.
9. Earl 1968, 77

BIBLIOGRAPHY

Agricola, Georgius 1556. *De Re Metallica* Translated by Hoover, H.C. & Hoover, L. H. 1950 (Dover Publications)

Austin, D, Gerrard, G.A.M. & Greeves, T.A.P. 1989. 'Tin & agriculture in the middle ages & beyond: Landscape archaeology in St Neot Parish Cornwall' *Cornish Archaeol.* **28**, 7-251

Amery, J. S. 1924. 'Presidential Address' *Rep Trans Devonshire Ass*, **56**, 43-102

Anon 1670. 'An Accompt of some Mineral Observations touching the Mines of Cornwall and Devon; etc' *Philosophical Transactions*

Beare, Thomas 1586. *Bailiff of Blackmoor* Transcribed and edited by J. A. Buckley, 1994 (Penhellick)

Bird, R. & Hirst, P. 1997. *The Brimpts Tin Mines, Dartmeet* (Dartmoor Tinworking Research Group)

Broughton, D. G. 1968-9. 'The Birch Tor and Vitifer Mining Complex' *Trans Cornish Inst of Engineers*, **24**, 25-49

Burnard, R. 1887-90. 'On the track of the "Old Men", Dartmoor' Part 1, & Part 2 *Trans Plymouth Instit*, **10**, 95-112; 223-242

Burnard, R. 1911. 'Presidential Address ' *Rep Trans Devonshire Ass.* **43**, 44-62

Carew, R. 1602. *Survey of Cornwall*

Chope, R. Pearse 1918. *Early Tours of Devon and Cornwall*

Claughton, P. 1996. 'The Lumbern Leat - evidence for new pumping technology at Bere Ferrers in the 15th century' in, Newman, P. (Ed) *The Archaeology of Mining and Metallurgy in South-West Britain.*

Cooke, R. M. L, Greeves, T.A.P. & Kilvington, C.C. 1974. 'Eylesbarrow(1814-1852). A study of a Dartmoor tin mine ' *Rep Trans Devonshire Ass*, **106**, 161-21 4

De la Beche, H.T. 1839. *Report on the Geology of Cornwall, Devon and West Somerset*

Earl, B. 1968. *Cornish Mining* (D. Bradford Barton)

Finberg, H.P.R. 1949. 'The Stannary of Tavistock' *Rep Trans Devonshire Ass*, **81**, 155-184

Fleming, A. & Ralph, N. 1982. 'Medieval settlement and land use on Holne Moor, Dartmoor: the landscape evidence' *Medieval Archaeol* **26**, 101-137

Fox, A. 1957. 'Excavations on Dean Moor in the Avon Valley, 1954-1956 (The late Bronze-Age settlement)' *Rep Trans Devonshire Ass*, **89**, 18-77

Gerrard, S. 1987. 'Streamworking in medieval Cornwall' *Jour. of the Trevithick Society*, **14**, 7-31

Gerrard, S. 1989. 'The medieval and early modern Cornish stamping mill' *Industrial Archaeology Review*, **12.1**, 9-19

Gerrard, S. 1996. 'The Early South-Western Tin Industry: An Archaeological View' in Newman, P.(ed) *The Archaeology of Mining and Metallurgy in South-West Britain* 67-83

Gerrard, S. 1997a. *Dartmoor* (English Heritage & Bastsford)

Gerrard, S. 1997b. *Lydford Woods Alluvial Tin Streamwork: A Report on Fieldwork carried out during 1994-5* (Unpub. report)

Gerrard, S. & Greeves, T. 1992. 'Summary Report on the Excavation of Upper Merrivale Tin Blowing & Stamping mill' *DTRG Newsletter*, **2**, 4

Gerrard, S. & Greeves, T. 1993. 'Summary Report on the 2nd Season of Excavation at Upper Merrivale Tin Blowing & Stamping Mill 1992' *DTRG Newsletter*, **4**, 4
Greeves, T.A.P, 1978. 'Wheal Cumpston Tin Mine, Holne, Devon' *Rep Trans Devonshire Ass*, **110,** 161-171
Greeves, T.A.P. 1981. *The Devon tin industry, 1450-1750: an archaeological and historical survey*. Univ Exeter Unpublished PhD thesis.
Greeves, T.A.P. 1985. 'Steeperton Tor Mine, Dartmoor, Devon' *Rep Trans Devonshire Ass*, **117,** 101-127
Greeves, T. 1986. *Tin Mines and Miners of Dartmoor*
Greeves, T.A.P. 1987. 'The Great Courts or Parliaments of the Devon Tinners 1484-1786' *Rep Trans Devonshire Ass*, **119**, 145-167
Greeves, T.A.P. 1987a. 'A note on the documentary evidence for openworks described in P Newman's survey' *Rep Trans Devonshire Ass*, **119,** 238-240 (Appendix to Newman 1987)
Greeves, T.A.P. 1992. 'Four Devon Stannaries: a comparitive study of tinworking in the sixteenth century' In Gray, T et al(eds) *Tudor and Stuart Devon - The Common Estate and Government*, 39-74
Hamilton Jenkin A.K. 1974. *Mines of Devon Volume 1: The Southern Area*
Harris, H. 1968. *Industrial Archaeology of Dartmoor*
Hitchens, F. & Drew, S. 1824. *The History of Cornwall from the Earliest Records and Traditions to the Present time*
Homer, R. F. 1995. 'Exeter Pewterers from the Fourteenth Century to about 1750' *Rep Trans Devonshire Ass.* **127**, 57-79
Kelly, J. 1866. 'Celtic remains on Dartmoor ' *Rep Trans Devonshire Ass.* **19(5)1,** 45-48
Le Messurier, B. 1979. 'The Post-Prehistoric Structures of Central North Dartmoor - a field survey' *Rep Trans Devonshire Ass.* **111**, 59-73
Moore, S. & Birkett, P. 1890. *A Short History of the Rights of Common upon The Forest of Dartmoor and The Commons of Devon* (Dartmoor Preservation Association)
Newman, P. 1987. 'The moorland Meavy - a tinners' landscape' *Rep Trans Devonshire Ass*, **119**, 223-240
Newman, P. 1987b. 'Two Small Mines in the Newleycombe Valley' *Dartmoor Magazine*, **8,** 8-10
Newman, P. 1994. 'Tinners and tenants on south-west Dartmoor: a case study in landscape history' *Rep Trans Devonshire Ass*, **126**, 199-238
Newman, P. 1996. 'Recording the Tinworks of Dartrmoor Forest' in Newman, P. (ed) *The Archaeology of Mining and Metallurgy in South-West Britain* 143-9
Polwhele, Richard 1797. *History of Devonshire*
Pryce, W. 1778. *Mineralogia Cornubiensis*, reprinted 1972(D Bradford Barton)
Radford, Lady 1930. 'Notes on the Tinners of Devon and their Laws Rep' *Rep Trans Devonshire Ass*, **62**, 225-247
Richardson, P.H.G. 1992. *Mines of Dartmoor and the Tamar Valley after 1913*
Risdon, T. 1714. *The Chorographic Description or Survey of the County of Devon*
Worth, R. Hansford 1953. *Dartmoor*
W.S.B.H (init.) 1923. 'Clasiewell Pool, Dartmoor' *Devon & Cornwall Notes & Queries* **12.5**, 238-9

GLOSSARY

Adit a tunnel which is cut horizontally into the hillside and used in underground mining for drainage and access, often associated with a tramway.

Beam/Beamwork large steep sided gully where tin was worked using opencast methods. See also Gert and openwork.

Bearing stone a rock, usually granite, into which a semi-circular slot has been cut on the upper face to support the rotating iron axles of a waterwheel or other machinary. The slots are usually worn smooth through continuous use.

Blowing mill/house stone buildings where tin was smelted in a blast furnace, with bellows powered by a waterwheel.

Buddle rectangular or circular pit in which previously crushed ore is concentrated by separation and settling in water.

Cassiterite tin oxide. The main ore source for tin.

Castle an early blast furnace for smelting tin..

Crazing mill a devise for crushing tin to a fine powder using two circular millstones in the manner of a corn mill.

Flat rod reciprocating iron rods powered by a waterwheel and passing over a system of supporting posts, which transmitted power to pumping equipment, often some distance from the wheel.

Floatstone a rectangular block of granite with a shallow elongated, rectangular hollow on its upper surface which was located in the base of the furnace to collect molten tin during smelting.

Furnace an open fronted hearth located in tin blowing mills, made from substantial pieces of granite, in which tin was smelted using a forced draught. Few survive.

Gert see beam.

Gangue a mixture of unwanted minerals associated with cassiterite deposits which are separated from the tin as part of the extraction and refining process.

Growan a stage in the decomposition process of granite where it has broken down into a course, crumbly gravel.

Launder a three-sided wooden channel forming part of a leat through which water could be diverted, usually to the top of a water wheel.

Leat an artificial water course which diverted water from river or hillwash sources to the tinworks and tin mills for various purposes.

Lodeback pit method of extracting lode tin where a series of confluent, interconnecting pits are dug down onto the back of the tin lode.

Mine a term usually used to describe a working where the lodes are exploited from underground via a system of shafts and adits.

Mortarstone a hard, flat-faced stone, usually granite, onto which water powered hammers or stamps would crush the mined ore.

Mouldstone large granite rock with rectangular indentations on the upper surface into which molten tin was cast into ingots.

Openwork see beam.

Overshot where the water supply for a waterwheel passes over the top of the wheel, turning the wheel in the same direction as the leat flow.

Pitchback where the water supply for a waterwheel, on reaching the top of the wheel, doubles back on itself turning the wheel in the opposite direction to the main leat flow.

Plumber block a bearing for supporting the axle of a waterwheel consisting of iron shoes cut into a masonry block.

Scarp a steep usually artificial slope which marks the edge of a tinwork..

Shaft vertical tunnel giving access to a mine and connecting to the horizontal levels. The shaft would be used for ventilation and to accommodate pumping equipment.

Stamping mill a building or other location where water-powered, vertically reciprocating hammers crushed the mined ore.

Stannary a district, of which in Devon there were four (Plympton, Tavistock, Chagford and Ashburton), from which the tin industry was administered and regulated.

Stope the area of an undergound adit where the lode is exposed. This may be on the floor of the adit known as an underhand stope, or above called an overhand stope.

Stoping the act of working a stope.

Streamworking a system of exploiting alluvial and eluvial tin gravels by digging down into the deposit and separating the tin from unwanted minerals using a stream of water.

Wheelpit a rectangular stone structure, usually buried or part-buried, which housed a waterwheel.

INDEX